PEKING

Peking

by
ODILE CAIL

EUGENE FODOR
Editor

MARY JANE SHIELDS
Associate Editor

PETER THOMSON
Art sketches and plans

Illustrated edition with map and city plans

DAVID MCKAY COMPANY INC.—NEW YORK

Travel Books Edited by Eugene Fodor

1936 ON THE CONTINENT
1937 IN EUROPE
EUROPE IN 1938
MEN'S GUIDE TO EUROPE
WOMEN'S GUIDE TO EUROPE
FODOR-SHELL TRAVEL GUIDES, U.S.A. (8 volumes)

1972 Area Guides, Revised Yearly

EUROPE
JAPAN AND EAST ASIA
CARIBBEAN, BAHAMAS AND BERMUDA
SOUTH AMERICA
INDIA
MEXICO
EUROPE ON A BUDGET
EUROPE UNDER 25

1972 Country Guides, Revised Yearly

AUSTRIA	IRELAND
BELGIUM AND LUXEMBOURG	ISRAEL
CZECHOSLOVAKIA	ITALY
FRANCE	MOROCCO
GERMANY	PORTUGAL
GREAT BRITAIN	SCANDINAVIA
GREECE	SPAIN
HAWAII	SWITZERLAND
HOLLAND	TURKEY
HUNGARY	YUGOSLAVIA

Companion City Guides

LONDON
ROME
VENICE

PRINTED IN THE UNITED STATES OF AMERICA

VAN REES PRESS

TABLE OF CONTENTS

v

TABLE OF CONTENTS

THE FACE OF PEKING

TABLE OF CONTENTS

—The museum of Stone Drums—The museum of Clocks—The treasures of the Ch'ing dynasty

MAPS AND PLANS

TABLE OF CONTENTS

EDITOR'S FOREWORD

A stringent sense of place and an inward-looking state of mind are characteristics of the Chinese. Their view of the world is completely egocentric: the Middle Kingdom is the hub of the earth, all other countries and civilizations are merely spokes.

The epicenter of the hub is 4000-year-old Peking, the core of Chinese power, culture, and ideology. Thus, Peking is, according to the Chinese, the center of the world. We might argue with this grandiose concept, but true or false, Peking is undoubtedly the most curiosity-provoking city in the world today.

Enigmatic China cannot be understood without knowing Peking. The very essence of the immense country, the capital is like no other. It hugs the earth in the manner of traditional Chinese city-planning rather than pointing skyward with high-rise buildings, such as most large cities. First and foremost, Peking is the complete showcase of classic Chinese art and architecture (the Imperial City alone contains over 80 palaces and major monuments). Peking also acts as a kind of Vatican City for the Maoist dogma and revolutionary institutions. It is the administrative, educational, industrial, and functional capital of the largest nation on earth.

For all of its alien fascination, it is the habitat of some seven million souls who lead surprisingly ordinary lives at a rhythm that is more small-townish than big-city, with many of their age-old ways intact. These are the Peking locals, a complex people full of apparent contradictions. They are extremely hard working, frugal-looking in their drab garb, and when viewed at their morning mass-exercises or holiday parades, they act fanatically disciplined, all waving their little red books in unison. Yet these same people have a passion for good food and good conversation, they are addicted to daily siestas, and love to loaf in the parks. In the final analysis, they may not be so frighteningly different or impossible to understand as at first we might think.

Visiting with them will add up to an adventure that is full of the thrills of the ultimate culture-shock—tempered by glimpses of people-to-people recognition.

In the aftermath of President Nixon's visit, we dedicate this book to the anticipation that Peking will soon open wide its Gates of Earthly Peace and Heavenly Peace. Then the Forbidden City will not be off-limits too much longer to the rest of the world, which is so eager to come. . . .

ଷଷଷଷ

The author of this guide, Mme. Odile Cail, is a French writer of considerable renown. Her first book on Peking was published in Paris several years ago. Mme. Cail is married to Jean-Pierre Rémy, a French career diplomat-author, who attained fame with a monumental novel on Peking during the Cultural Revolution, *The Sack of the Summer Palace*. The book was written while the couple was posted at the French Embassy in Peking, a tenure of several years.

Sorbonne-educated, with years of diplomatic experience in Peking, Hong Kong, and London, Mme. Cail is also a culinary expert, an art specialist, and a general China-culture buff. Her total expertise permitted us to dispense with our usual method of using a team of specialists for books of this kind. Mme. Cail structured this guide in our own editorial pattern, so that only some practical material had to be added to fill the specific needs of the traveler to China from the Western Hemisphere. We plan to enlarge this *Guide to Peking* into a complete Guide to China, as soon as we are permitted to explore the rest of the country.

FACTS AT YOUR FINGERTIPS

FACTS AT YOUR FINGERTIPS

The Climate. Peking is a town that changes with the seasons more than any other world capital. Winter makes it an imposing and splendidly austere city, under the loveliest light you can imagine. But summer makes it human: patches of green appear among the uniform gray and yellow of the rooftops, as Peking becomes a multitude of gardens enclosed between the houses.

So what is the best time to go? Tourists are generally advised to go in autumn. Then the climate is warm and gentle, and splendid sunsets linger over the russet woodlands of the western hills, while the impressive ceremonies of the First of October unfurl their processions and popular festivities. It is the season when the trees are heavy with red *kaki* fruit and the streets are full of entertainments.

Winter is very cold and dry. But if you don't mind temperatures below 20° C (−4° F), as well as a wind from Mongolia that takes you by the throat, you can discover empty lunar landscapes under a pure azure sky, and Peking will seem more than ever a timeless city. You must simply remember that the days will be short and that evenings in the hotel bedrooms of the Hsin Chiao or the Peking Hotel are not wildly amusing. Above all, don't come to Peking in winter to look at the snow: there isn't any.

FACTS AT YOUR FINGERTIPS

Spring comes officially to China at the beginning of the lunar year, that is, some time in February. A somewhat premature spring: it is still very cold, and for a few hours the year's only snowflakes may be falling. But from the end of March until mid-May the temperature gets gradually milder, the sun shines more and more, the trees burst into leaf, the lilacs and peonies bloom. The first rains arrive too, but they are light rains, not likely to trouble the visitor.

Finally summer comes: at first dry and hot, from the end of May to early July, then damp and still hot in July and August—30° – 40° C (86°–104° F). Though it is much more bearable than Hong Kong, for example, the hot season is not the best time to visit Peking. Hotel bedrooms are not air-conditioned, and the sun beats down scorchingly on the Great Wall and on the road to the Ming Tombs.

WAYS OF GETTING TO PEKING

Distance—a remoteness less geographical than political and psychological—makes a journey to China a rather mysterious kind of expedition, despite its relative simplicity. You can in fact get to Peking with little trouble—provided you have a visa (see below). You simply buy a ticket at a travel agency.

By Air. There are three airlines serving China from the West: *Air France, Aeroflot,* and *Pakistan International Airlines* *(PIA).* Other airlines are cautiously and without publicity negotiating with China for landing rights, among them *Pan Am. TWA* obtained CAB approval in 1947 to include Canton and Shanghai in its routes, but service was never started. The airline is at present reapplying to the CAB to serve Canton. Also seeking a route is *CP Air* (formerly *Canadian Pacific Air*).

For an American with a visa the least expensive way to get to Peking is to fly to Hong Kong and take the train from there to Canton and then a train or plane to Peking. Round-trip costs by this indirect and somewhat time-consuming route would be a total of about $1,180. Costs from Los Angeles would be about $941. (See below.)

BY AIR FROM U.S./CANADA TO HONG KONG

Gateway	Airline, frequency	Round-trip fare
New York	*Pan Am, TWA, Northwest*—daily	$1,049
Chicago	*Northwest*—daily	981
Los Angeles	*Pan Am, TWA, Northwest*—daily	811
Minneapolis	*Northwest*—daily	981
St. Louis	*TWA*—daily	981
San Francisco	*TWA, Northwest*—daily	811
Seattle	*Northwest*—daily	811
Anchorage	*Northwest*—daily	811
Montreal	*CP Air*—3 a week	1,015
Ottawa	*CP Air*—3 a week	1,015
Vancouver	*CP Air*—3 a week	811

Note: Flights are direct from New York and Chicago. Fares are 14/21-day economy-class excursion fares. First-class fares are about $700 higher.

FACTS AT YOUR FINGERTIPS

Among the direct routes are New York–Paris–Shanghai, with *Air France* giving you two flights weekly from which to choose. One *Air France* flight leaves Paris on Monday, arrives in Shanghai on Tuesday, and turns around that day for the return flight to France. The second flight leaves Paris on Saturday, stopping in Karachi and Rangoon, and arriving in Shanghai on Sunday; the plane leaves the same day on its return. The round-trip New York–Paris–Shanghai flight costs $1,515. The fare on *PIA* from New York–London–Karachi–Shanghai is $1,549, only slightly more expensive than going on *Air France* via Paris. Least expensive of the direct routes, though involving more red tape, is *Aeroflot*'s routing, New York–London–Moscow–Peking, at a price of $1,384 round trip. Fares quoted are 14/21-day excursion, economy class.

Americans going via Hong Kong will have to transfer at the border to a train to Canton, connecting there to Peking. Cost from Hong Kong to Peking is little—about $65—but the whole trip from the United States and Canada will take three to four days.

BY AIR FROM OTHER CITIES TO CHINA

Gateway	Destination	Airline, frequency	Round-trip fare
Paris	Shanghai	*Air France*, 2 a week	$1,162.20
Athens	Shanghai	*Air France*, 1 a week	1,077.00
Cairo	Shanghai	*Air France*, 1 a week	1,027.00
Moscow	Peking	*Aeroflot*, 1 a week	691.20
Irkutsk	Peking	*Aeroflot*, 1 a week	280.00
London	Shanghai (via Karachi)	*Pakistan Int'l (PIA)*, 2 a week	1,227.00
London	Canton (via Karachi)	*PIA*, 1 a week	1,200.60
Karachi	Shanghai	*PIA*, 2 a week	602.80
Karachi	Canton	*PIA*, 1 a week	470.80

The *Chinese Airline*, a domestic service operated by China's Civil Aviation Administration, has twice-weekly flights from Hanoi, once-weekly flights from Pyongyang, North Korea, via Shenyang, and from Rangoon. *North Korea's airline* also flies once a week to Peking via Shenyang.

Other airfare quotations you may need in calculating transportation to China via Hong Kong or European cities:

Gateway	Destination	Airline, frequency	Round-trip fare
New York	London ⎤	any major carrier, daily	$322.00
New York	Paris ⎦		353.00
Tokyo	Hong Kong	*Japan Air Lines*, daily	326.80
Canton	Peking	*Chinese Airline*, 5 times weekly	198.40
Shanghai	Canton	*Chinese Airline*, weekly	126.00
		PIA, weekly	126.00
Shanghai	Peking	*Chinese Airline*, 6 times weekly	122.00

Note: Fares on international routes in the two charts above are 14/21-day economy-class excursion fares.

5

FACTS AT YOUR FINGERTIPS

By Boat. The days are past—regrettably, perhaps—when a trip to the Orient began with a month's cruise. But you can still get to China this way if you have the time. Companies such as the *Orient Overseas Line* (*E.H. Mundy & Co., Ltd.,* 60 East 2nd St., New York, N.Y. 10017) can organize a voyage for you from Britain or from San Francisco.

By Train. Ambitious travelers—those who want a China adventure and a Russia adventure in the same trip—might consider taking the train from Moscow across Siberia to Peking. The journey from London or Paris to Peking lasts eight days (two to Moscow, six to Peking); it is long and monotonous, but also the cheapest of the approach routes to China. There are two routes—one through Mongolia, one through Manchuria—but on either one you have to change trains at the heavily guarded border.

On the Manchuria line, Moscow to Peking, the one-way first-class (two-berth compartment) fare is $132; occupancy in a four-berth compartment costs slightly less, $118. Second-class one-way fare, with four passengers in a compartment, is only $83. Trains leave Moscow on Tuesday and Friday, and the trip takes six days, four hours.

On the Mongolia line, Moscow to Peking, a one-way first-class ticket for a two-berth compartment is $138, for a four-berth compartment $121; second-class fare is $86. The train leaves Moscow on Wednesday for the five-day journey.

A round-trip ticket from London to Moscow costs $170 first class, $128 second class.

Traveling second class means wooden sleeping berths, but it puts the trip from Western Europe to Peking within the range of modest travel budgets. It is, however, very tiring, and you should bring a sleeping bag with you, for use at least as a mattress.

To the cost of the ticket add from $2 to $3.50 a day for food. Plan your trip carefully, since there are only two trains a week from Moscow.

Americans who fly from the United States to Hong Kong have to walk across the border where they can take a comfortable train to Canton, a four-hour trip. You can continue to Peking by train or take the plane for $39 one way. You can also go from Canton to Shanghai by comfortable air-conditioned train; the trip, however, takes twenty-five and one half hours.

Package Tours to China. The time of mass travel to China is a long way off, if indeed it ever comes. It is not China's policy to grant individual visas to Americans other than VIPs, important journalists, and members of highly specialized groups whose purpose is not sightseeing. Despite the formidable obstacles, a number of tour operators have made plans for package tours for groups of tourists, and they are keeping lists of interested persons against the day China's door opens wider.

Apparently working closely with Mao's government is the *Skyline Travel Service* (1148 West Georgia St., Vancouver, B.C.). While strongly discouraging publicity about its plans and about tourism to China in general, Skyline has packaged a 21-day tour for special-interest groups, presumably approved by Peking. It has wholesaled it to at least two American travel agencies, *Murphey Travel Service* (552 Lincoln Ave., Winnetka, Ill., 60093) and *Carnival Travel* (3701A Southwest Trafficway, Kansas City, Mo., 64111).

Itinerary for this trip, which would cost $1,850, starts with an overnight briefing in Vancouver and a Chinese meal with departure by *CP Air* for Hong Kong. After two nights (one day), Peking (four days), Shanghai (three days), Hangchow (two days), and back to Canton (three days), ending with another day in Hong Kong before a return flight to Vancouver.

The price would include single- or twin-bed accommodations, all meals including catered meals in China, sightseeing, bus and rail transportation, guide and interpreter services, and all entrance fees.

As of early 1972 no visas had been granted to any hopeful participants in this package tour.

Two travel agencies have plans for trips but, so far, no approval has come from Peking. Optimistic *American Express* (65 Broadway, New York, N.Y., 10006) has twelve provisional Saturday departures from April to October 1972 for a 22-day tour costing $1,850. If the package materializes, and its participants receive visas, they would fly from San Francisco or Los Angeles to Hong Kong for a three-day stay before taking the train to Canton (three days). They would fly to Shanghai (three days), taking a side trip to Soochow, then continue on to Peking (three days) and back to Canton (three days) before catching the train back to Hong Kong. The China visitors would stay overnight in Hong Kong, then fly back to the West Coast. The price would include double occupancy in hotels, meals, fully escorted sightseeing, transfers, and all necessary transportation.

Lindblad Travel, Inc. (133 East 55th St., New York, N.Y. 10022) looks to 1973 to begin its 18-day "China Expedition" cruise. Eight times from May to October the motorship *Lindblad Explorer* would sail along the China coast from Hong Kong, with calls at Canton, Shanghai, Tientsin (three-day stopover with day trips to Peking, among other places), Hangchow, and Portuguese Macao. The ship would serve as hotel accommodations for the cruise, which would cost $1,800, including all meals, sightseeing, and lectures.

How to Get Your Visa: Getting to China is not quite the same as going from the United States to other overseas countries open to Americans. Securing a visa to China remains a long and hazardous undertaking, not always crowned with success. With a few special exceptions, individual visits are, as a rule, rejected; only some special interest groups—an anti-Vietnam war group of important American China scholars, for example—have been allowed in. Your chances of getting an individual visa soon are not good, unless you are Henry Kissinger or a *New York Times* correspondent.

The first step is to go to the Chinese Embassy in one of those capitals that have diplomatic relations with Peking. In Europe these are Berne, Copenhagen, Oslo, Stockholm, Helsinki, The Hague, London, and Paris. The only Chinese Embassy in North America is in Ottawa.

The easiest course for Americans with a desire at least to get their names on the list of hopeful China tourists is to write a letter giving

FACTS AT YOUR FINGERTIPS

background information on yourself (indicate any political affiliations and religious beliefs) and stating the purpose of your visit and proposed length of stay. The letter should be addressed to:

Cultural Department
Embassy of the People's Republic of China
100 Bronson Ave.
Ottawa, Ontario, Canada
(Tel. 613-234-4721)
or
International Travel Bureau
Peking, China

If you drop in at a Chinese Embassy, you will be received with the greatest courtesy. If you are not discouraged from continuing your efforts, you will eventually have to fill in numerous questionnaires.

The embassy or consulate will probably urge you strongly—if you get to *this* stage—to have your trip organized in advance by the China Travel Service. If you tell them you do not want to do this, it is still possible to get a visa; simply ask them to book a hotel room for you in Peking and tell them that you will organize the details of your stay when you get there. This is the best solution: the staff of the Peking branch of the China Travel Service is extremely friendly and relatively efficient, and if you want to use their services it is much better to do so when you arrive than to have things arranged in advance.

Don't forget that if you are traveling via Moscow or Hong Kong and want to stop over in either city for a few days, you must obtain an entry visa from a Soviet consulate or, unless you are a British national, at a British consulate for Hong Kong.

No one who applies for a visa to China should be optimistic about getting it quickly: the record speed is two weeks.

Vaccination. You need a smallpox vaccination less than three years old to enter China, just as you do to enter the United States. For Hong Kong you need a cholera vaccination less than six months old.

How long to stay. Time hasn't the same meaning in China as in the West. The Chinese tourist services have, it is true, drawn up whirlwind programs for those visitors who enjoy going round the world, seeing how many cities they can visit in the shortest possible time. But the capital of "the greatest people on earth" deserves three weeks' rather than three days' attention. You can't be advised too strongly to stay at least two or three weeks in Peking if you want to try to understand the soul of this city while at the same time admiring its monuments and museums. Few towns create such a feeble initial impression in the hurried visitor, but few towns are so rich in hidden beauties or in picturesque scenes of daily life, if only you give yourself time to seek them out.

 Money and cost of living. The official Chinese currency unit is the *yuan*, called also *kuai* ("unit"). A yuan is worth about $.40 and is divided into 10 *mao*, while the mao in turn is divided into 10 *fen*.

FACTS AT YOUR FINGERTIPS

Thus there are 100 fen in a yuan. There are coins of 1, 2, and 5 yuan, the 5-yuan note being worth $2.08. This 5-yuan note is the largest Chinese currency denomination, and this can cause problems—on leaving an exchange office, you can find your wallet turned into a sort of briefcase!

In Peking all foreign currencies, including American dollars, are accepted and changed for yuan. Travelers' checks, except those denoted in American dollars or issued by American banks, are also accepted; the American tourist would thus be well advised to purchase traveler's checks in a foreign currency.

When you arrive in China, you will be given a printed declaration of currency importation to fill out, and you will be asked for it when you leave the country. Keep this document carefully and see that the correct entry is made on it each time you change money.

Life is not expensive in Peking. A hotel room costs an average of 10 to 14 yuan a day, an average meal about 4 yuan, and a taxi ride between 2 and 6 yuan, but the distances are enormous. As for shopping (see pages 88–98), you will have plenty of opportunity to notice just how cheap things are.

 Customs: what you can bring in and out. On arrival you must also submit for inspection a series of objects, from your watch to your camera: if you don't, you'll have the greatest trouble in getting them out again. So don't lose the document that you have filled in and that an official has approved.

In principle, you are not allowed to bring into China books or magazines hostile to the regime. In fact, it is very difficult for the customs officials to enforce this ban, and they generously turn a blind eye to any literature you bring in with you. On the other hand, the cigarettes (two-hundred) and spirits (one bottle) that you can bring in duty-free are more strictly controlled.

Finally, if while you are in China you receive a parcel from abroad, you must pay a 200-percent duty on its value. This makes some presents rather expensive.

 Taking photographs. In principle, you are free to photograph what you want in Peking, except for "military installations" and individuals whose permission you have not sought. In fact, "military installations" can include the most innocent old bridge or even a house inhabited by some leading figure of the regime. So you must be careful where you point your camera. They also take it very much amiss if you photograph a slum district or a squalid street: zealous militants may even go as far as to try to take your camera away and destroy the film in it, claiming that you are "taking pictures of Chinese poverty to sell to the Americans!" But don't let them browbeat you: demand to be escorted to a police station (that is, if you can make yourself understood; if not, simply stand your ground) and ask for an interpreter. On most occasions matters will simply rest there. In any event, dont give up your film except as a last resort.

Legally you have no right to take undeveloped film out of China.

So you should in theory get your film developed and printed while you are there. In fact, this rule is never applied: they simply ask you to use only those types of film that can, if necessary, be developed in China.

Basic necessities, to buy or bring with you. China is not a country where there is nothing to buy. But lots of things are lacking.

Tobacco: Chinese cigarette tobacco is very pungent. Watch out!

Wines and spirits: no strong drinks of a European type are on sale in Peking, except vodka.

Books: you will find no books in English, French, German, Spanish, etc., in Peking. On the other hand, you can find every kind of political pamphlet, anti-imperialist or anti-revisionist, that you could wish for.

Pharmaceuticals: Chinese medicines are excellent and very cheap. The only trouble is explaining what you want.

Clothes: see above on the seasons for rough guidance. Here are some more details:

May to September: take very light clothes, but bring an umbrella. In Peking you can buy marvelous oiled-paper umbrellas for 36 cents.

October to November: light clothing but also a warm jacket.

End of November to end of March: very warm clothing.

April: rather less warm clothing.

You can see that spring does not exist and autumn is short.

Shoes: Men can safely take what they like, bearing in mind the temperature and the summer rains. But women should avoid high heels in the streets of Peking: you will not be comfortable and whole crowds will stare at you. Men and women alike should bring rubber-soled shoes for going to the Great Wall in winter, if you don't want to slip on the flagstones, which are not only frozen over but often incline at a 45° angle.

THE PEKING SCENE

A CITY THAT IS DIFFERENT

First of all, a warning: Peking is different from anything you already know or can imagine. You have to be there only a few hours to feel yourself in a cultural vacuum, deprived of a hundred comfortable assumptions you always took for granted. For us Westerners, Peking is a city empty of clues. Hence this book. It isn't meant to analyze the city's political or philosophical background, an attempt that belongs to a different sort of book altogether. Instead, it sets out to provide some clues to life as it is lived there. I want to help you see over the barriers of strangeness and difference to discover the fascinations of Peking past and present, and so take back from China an experience you can get nowhere else. But before you reserve your ticket, there are some things you should know.

A town unlike any other

Peking is a town like none other. Visiting China in 1910, a young French naval doctor, Victor Segalen, described it to his

13

friend Debussy as one single triumphal way leading between temples and palaces from south to north, with a mass of little low gray houses, on either side, all exactly the same. Modern districts have risen beyond the acres of little houses, but the impact on today's newly arrived tourist is still much what it was half a century ago: a vast bare square, an avenue three times as wide as Fifth Avenue or the Champs Élysées and practically empty, a red gate to the north, a gray gate to the south. And that, it seems, is Peking. Where's the town? Where's the center? Perhaps only a visitor from Los Angeles, a city equally scattered, shapeless, and centerless in its very different way, might feel vaguely at home here.

It is disconcerting to travel six or seven thousand miles in search of the capital of the largest nation on earth—only to find when you get there that it doesn't exist. Some travelers never recover from the shock. But Peking is a town that reveals its character only to the people who search it out.

This character hasn't really changed for fifty years, even five hundred years. In spite of new buildings thrown up to accommodate the major political bodies of the new China, and the suburbs of severe working-class housing stretching into the distance, the little houses and the *hutung* (alleyways of old Peking) still form the essential basis of the town. Other capitals in other countries, from Lima to Moscow, from Léopoldville to Djakarta, have something in common. Peking does not share it. Don't look here for what makes up a town in the rest of the world—opulent late-nineteenth-century housing or the first sprouting of skyscrapers; big department stores like Macy's or hotels with lush lobbies.

Peking has never been an international city. At the beginning of this century, when the seeds of Western civilization were scattered across the world, it was Shanghai, and to a lesser degree Tientsin, that drew the attention of Western speculators and businessmen. Peking, the political capital, restricted foreigners to a small Legation District whose residents left few traces of their discreet intrusion.

Today, in this huge city of 8 million souls, nothing has changed. More closed to the West than ever, Peking has been spared many of its degrading influences. It is still a medieval town onto which have been grafted a few "modern" districts comically touching in their old-fashionedness. It took 1958 and the policy of the "Great Leap Forward" for the Chinese to start putting up an occasional building in the somberly imposing Soviet style. But these hardly change the town's original face. Peking remains outside time.

A town not to be visited like any other

This book has an aim: to allow you to leave your hotel, guidebook in hand, and see Peking. But few travelers have been able until now to do this, for Peking is not a town that you visit like any other. Those who traveled in Soviet Russia in the heroic days of the first tourist contacts may feel a bit blasé— "Oh, the Iron Curtain, we know all about that!" You may know the Iron Curtain, but you don't know Peking.

As in many other totalitarian countries, you aren't allowed to see everything in China. Only certain big towns are "open" —that is, you can go there if you get permission. Your journey will be by air or rail, but never by road. But excursions around Peking itself are also restricted: you cannot go more than fifteen miles from the center, except along a narrow corridor to the Ming Tombs or the Great Wall. And inside Peking, anything of any possible strategic interest is strictly banned to visitors. So you will occasionally come up against someone adamantly barring your way, but you are perfectly free to wander where you want, to penetrate into a courtyard or the most remote of the *hutung*.

To help you enjoy yourself, the Chinese tourist office (*Luxingshe*, or *China Travel Service*) has been created—an organization with its own cars, guides, and organized sight-seeing tours that leave little room for chance or private initia-tive. A stay in Peking "prepared" by Luxingshe allows the tourist to see everything that the State considers suitable. For, like most young countries, the new China has many little secrets, most of which are quite trivial, since the notion of what is "strategic" is open to wide interpretation. But the result is that the China Travel Service has a *de facto* monopoly over tourism. At first sight it might seem that you can't do anything without the C.T.S. Just finding your way in Peking can be a problem despite the apparent right-angle geometry of the streets: there is no good map of the town and street names are not written in Roman lettering. As for taxis, they scarcely exist except in front of three hotels and at Ch'ien Men, and it is useless to try to telephone for one unless you speak perfect Chinese—indeed, the language obstacle in Peking can discourage the most intrepid. In the face of so many difficulties, people tend to put themselves in the hands of the official services that show you what they want you to see.

There's the rub. In addition to the open secrets that fool no one, People's China anxiously conceals all that it regards as the shameful evidence of a feudal society now swept away by revolution: nearly everything—apart from two or three temples and the imperial palaces—that might be of greatest interest to the archaeologist, the art historian, or the simple art-lover, is deliberately left in the shadows. The past has been crossed out. China begins in 1949. The English-language Guide to Peking published by the C.T.S. devotes more pages to the various monuments built since 1958 than to the Forbidden City! Most of the city's temples are purely and simply ignored, whereas you don't have to make the slightest effort to get into the Palace of Congress, a people's commune, or the Museum of the Revolution.

This guide is not intended to lead you to neglect the official tourist services, whose good will is untiring, but to explain to you what else there is to see.

THUMBNAIL GUIDE TO CHINA'S CULTURE AND HISTORY

This book is intended not to provide a vast panorama of Chinese culture and history, from the remotest times to Mao's Republic, but to give you certain historical and artistic guide-points that will allow you to place correctly, in this timeless city, the principal monuments, the loveliest objects, and the most ancient beliefs. If you want to deepen your knowledge of these subjects, these are the major works:

FITZGERALD, CHARLES PATRICK, *China: A Short Cultural History*, 3rd ed., rev. (London: Cresset Press, 1961).

THE PEKING SCENE

McALEAVY, HENRY, *Modern History of China* (New York: Frederick A. Praeger, 1967).

SCHRAM, STUART R., *Mao Tse-tung* (New York: Simon & Schuster, 1967).

——, *Political Thought of Mao Tse-tung*, rev. ed. (New York: Frederick A. Praeger, 1969).

SNOW, EDGAR, *Red Star Over China*, rev. ed. (New York: Grove Press, 1968).

SULLIVAN, MICHAEL, *An Introduction to Chinese Art* (Berkeley: University of California Press, 1961).

WILSON, DICK, *Anatomy of China: An Introduction to One Quarter of Mankind* (New York: New American Library, 1969).

History: some dates and facts

The origins of Chinese civilization are lost in the mists of time. It all began with legend, from which it is hard to extract true history. After a fabulous "Father of the Universe," there came Three Kings, mythological figures who reigned over the earth, sky, and mankind.

C. 2700 B.C.   Around this date ruled Huang-ti, the first of the Five Emperors who make up, more or less, the first of the Chinese dynasties, but whose mythical existence is better established than their historical reality. Yao-ti, the fourth emperor, gave his people a useful present: the calendar, which regulated the moons and the seasons and protected them against the uncertainties of the heavens.

2600 B.C.: reign of Cheops in Egypt; building of the greatest Pyramids

C. 2200–1570 B.C.: Hsia dynasty   Yao was followed by Shun-ti, then by Yu the Great who founded the Hsia dynasty and discovered how to tame the rivers and prevent the floods that used to devastate all China. The Hsia reigned for nearly five centuries, but finally sank into tyranny and cruelty. Their seventeenth monarch, Chou-hsin, the very model of a wicked king, was overthrown by Cheng T'ang, who installed a new dynasty, that of the Shang (or Yin), who ruled for six centuries.

C. 1750–1110 B.C.: Shang (or Yin) dynasty

At this point we leave the epic period to enter true history. Following a cycle that has repeated itself throughout China's history, the Shang, like the Hsia and like the Ming at a later date, were at first enlightened monarchs and then gradually declined into corruption—only to be overthrown in their turn by the pure founders of a new dynasty, this time the mighty Chou.

1580–1090 B.C.: period of the Great Pharaohs in Egypt

C. 1110–475 B.C.: Chou dynasty

It was under the Chou that China really emerged. The capital of the kingdom was moved in the eighth century B.C. from Sian to Loyang, further east along the Yellow River, the great cradle of Chinese civilization; the social structures gradually took shape, while in the sixth century B.C. the two great guiding philosophers of China were born within a score of years of each other: Lao Tzu and Confucius. But from that time onward the House of Chou was in decline. Several clans confronted each other: the Chin from the Shansi, the Ch'in close by from the Shensi, the Ch'i, the Shantung, and the powerful southern monarchs of Hupeh, the Ch'ou.

C. 1200–1100 B.C.: Trojan Wars

551–479 B.C.: Confucius

753 B.C.: foundation of Rome

490 B.C.: Battle of Marathon 431–404 B.C.: Peloponnesian Wars

475–221 B.C.: period of the "warring states"

This was the period of the so-called "warring states," with each conquering the others in turn, until the complete victory in 221 B.C. of the Ch'in under Shih Huang-ti.

356–323 B.C.: Alexander the Great

THE PEKING SCENE

221–210
B.C.*: reign of Shi Huang-Ti*

For the first time in its history, China became a unified empire under the rule of a single monarch—and what a monarch! Shih Huang-ti has two great claims to fame: he built—or rather he completed—the Great Wall, and he was the emperor who acted the most disgracefully toward men of letters. He is credited with having "caused all the books to be burned." In fact, although he hated literature, he did preserve scientific works—and it was he who created China.

206 B.C.–
A.D. *25: Han dynasty*

In 206 the Han dynasty took power. The empire retained its unity and undertook the conquest of Asia. Under the emperor Wu, at the end of the second century B.C., the first contacts were made with the "barbarian" West of the Roman Empire. The "silk route" for trade became important. But as time passed the regime grew feeble, and when an incompetent monarch was overthrown by a usurper, the revolt of the "Red Eyebrows"—a movement both peasant and aristocratic—restored to the throne those today known as the "Later Han," who held power at

A.D. *25–220: dynasty of the "Later," or "Eastern," Han*

Loyang for two centuries. The Han marked the whole of China with their centralizing power, and from then on the Chinese were known as the sons of the Han.

220–c. 280: period of the "Three Kingdoms"

After a movement called the "Yellow Turbans" had brought down the last Han there came the famous episode of the "Three Kingdoms" that marked Chinese classical literature so deeply. After this, China fell into a

49–44 B.C.*:
Julius Caesar's dictatorship*

4 B.C.–A.D.
30: life of Jesus Christ

period of anarchy rich in spectacular events. Wars and invasions, famines and agrarian revolts followed one another. Briefly the land was reunified under the First Chin, but their successors were incapable of maintaining that central power that had proved the strength of the Han dynasty. From 420 to 581 two series of short-lived dynasties confronted each other in the north and south. Their conflicts were finally settled only with the conquest of China by the Sui in 581.

The reign of the Sui was short, but at least they reestablished the shattered unity of China. They undertook vast public works, such as the famous "grand canal"—but their dynasty was sharply cut short by the arrival of the T'ang.

Under the T'ang, China rediscovered her glory. It was a period of foreign conquest and national peace. A remarkably fair agrarian system led to the appeasement of most peasant demands; the mandarins enjoyed their moment of supreme splendor; the arts flourished as never before. And Buddhism, first introduced into China in the first century A.D., now spread over the entire land.

But the last of the T'ang monarchs was a disappointment. In 755 a revolt narrowly failed to overthrow him and the dynasty finally disappeared in 907 to give way to the rivalries of several regional kingdoms—a period known as that of the "Five Dynasties."

In 960 the Sung emerged to usher in the golden age of a well-ordered China, her intellectual riches greater

265–317: reign of the "First," or "Western," Chin

420–581: "Northern" and "Southern" dynasties

581–618: Sui dynasty

618–907: T'ang dynasty

960–1127: dynasty of the Northern Sung

307–337: reign of Constantine the Great (476): end of the Western Roman Empire

711: the Moors invade Spain

800–814: Empire of Charlemagne

1066: Norman Conquest

than ever before. Although the mandarin system began to degenerate into bureaucracy, painting remained admirable, and the first genuinely artistic works in porcelain appeared. China in this period was shaken by bold reforms and internal struggles, but kept its unity, until the Southern Sung took over from the Northern Sung.

1096–1270: the Crusades

1127–1276: dynasty of the Southern Sung

At the end of the thirteenth century China may be said to have entered modern history. A conqueror from the West, Genghis Khan, ravaged the whole of Asia and soon his hordes were battering on the gates of the Chinese Middle Empire. China's resistance was finally overcome, and Genghis' grandson, Kubla Khan—whom Marco Polo admired so much, and whom Coleridge dreamed about so poetically—mounted the throne of Peking.

1206–1227: Genghis Khan occupies part of northern China

1337: beginning of the Anglo-French Hundred Years War

1276: Kubla Khan takes Peking

In 1276 the last of the Sung were defeated, and the Mongol dynasty of the Yuan, cut off from their origins in Central Asia, reigned in Peking until 1368. Peking became the center of China, and the provincial capitals organized themselves on its model. The Court ceremonies became more and more refined. European ambassadors were received and Catholicism found a foothold in the shadow of the Imperial City. Arabs, Italians, and Mongols rubbed shoulders with the true sons of the Han in a rapidly expanding city.

1276–1368: Yuan dynasty (Mongol)

1378–1420: Papal Schism between Rome and Avignon

1368–1644: the Ming Dynasty

A national movement of insurrection against the Mongol occupiers culminated, in 1368, in the capture of

1453: capture of Constantinople by the Turks

Some glimpses of China's presence and importance to our world: 800 million energetic and industrious people, motivated by a revolutionary discipline of unprecedented intensity and scope. There is also the timeless China of the arts, architecture, and sciences, with its contributions to human civilization . . . *Photos: Odile Cail*

the throne by the Ming. Henceforth, China became the autocratic Empire in all its terrible magnificence. The emperor, Monarch of China, reigned as a true Son of the Heavens. It was the third Ming emperor, Yung Lo, who really built modern Peking: he collected the greatest library on earth and gave power to the eunuchs. From being at first the mere guardians of harems, these able men became powerful counselors, sworn enemies of the literary intellectuals whose place they had usurped. At the same time the social structure of the peasantry began to take firm shape, and a class of bourgeoisie and merchants, modest at first but influential, made its appearance. The great Jesuits from Portugal and Italy made their way to China— a new center of influence.

Fifteenth and sixteenth centuries: the Renaissance in Italy, France, etc.

Like other Chinese dynasties, the Ming were destroyed by their own corruption. Their last monarch, Ch'ung Cheng, hanged himself in 1644 on the Hill of Coal in Peking, while his enemies were invading the city. He had already had to face the famous rebel general Li Tsu-ch'eng. But the true victors of the Ming were not so much this general as the Manchu kings. Coming from Mukden, in the heart of present-day northeast China, these descendants of ancient tribes of Central Asia managed gradually to build up a solid empire quite close to Peking. After several abortive attempts at conquest, they were finally invited into China by the Chinese themselves in order to chase out Li Tsu-ch'eng. And thus in 1644 the

1492: Columbus discovers America

1661–1715: reign of Louis XIV in France

Manchu emperor Shun Chih mounted the throne of Peking.

The Ch'ing dynasty (the Manchu's official name) stayed in power till 1911. Its most notable leaders were K'ang Hsi, Yung Cheng, and above all Ch'ien Lung (1736–1796) and the dowager empress Tzu Hsi. Her role in the Imperial City's history is so important, and still so much alive, that it is worth looking at in detail. Born in 1835, she grew up to become an imperial concubine. She soon won an important place at the court, marrying the comic little emperor Hsien Feng and assuming the rank of his leading wife. But it was after the war of 1860, when British and French troops invaded Peking and sacked the Summer Palace, that she carried out the stunning coup that established her power. Hsien Feng had fled to Jehol, where he died. The empress, knowing that the family of the dead king was plotting her downfall, nevertheless accompanied his body to Peking, leaving her favorite, Lung Lu, to arrest the conspirators at the entrance to the town. They were severely punished as a warning to others; and Tzu Hsi was able to put her son T'ung Chih on the throne as Regent and hold all real power herself. After T'ung Chih's death she became still more despotic. Helped by a few intimate advisors—and it was suggested that they weren't all eunuchs —she managed to get rid of Tzu An, a rival dowager empress whom she loathed. Then in 1898 she shut up the young emperor Kuang Hsu on an

1644–1911: Ch'ing (Manchu) dynasty

1860: British and French troops invade Peking

1860–1908: effective reign of Tzu Hsi

1776: United States becomes independent

1789: French Revolution

1799–1815: Napoleonic Wars

1854: Japan opens its doors to foreigners

1861–1865: American Civil War

island in the South Lake of the imperial gardens, and kept him there until he died. It was Tzu Hsi who directly supported the Boxer rebels in 1900.

1904–1905: Russo-Japanese War

1900: Boxer Rebellion

In 1908 Tzu Hsi and Kuang Hsu died within a few hours of each other. (Rumor has it that the latter was strangled on Tzu Hsi's orders.) The young Hsuan T'ung, who succeeded to the throne, stayed on it only three years. In 1911 the first Chinese revolution swept away the last of the Manchu sovereigns and the Empire itself. One curious detail is that Hsuan T'ung later became the prince of the short-lived Manchukuo state set up by the Japanese, and then in 1964 under his simple commoner's name of Pu Yi he was elected to the National Assembly of the Chinese People! *From Emperor to Citizen* is the title of his autobiography, recently published in Peking, in which he tells how, in the years before 1964, he was a simple gardener. His amazing story begins with the Boxer Rebellion and goes on, from one revolution to another, till the sixteenth year of the new regime.

1911: first Chinese revolution; fall of Empire

1914–1918: First World War

The Birth of the regime: After Yuan Shi-k'ai's short-lived attempt (1912–16) to restore the monarchy, and the dark years of anarchy that followed it, the history of China until 1949 is simply that of a long revolution and of the gradual seizure of power by the Communist Party.

1912–1916: Yuan Shi-k'ai tries to restore the Empire

1917: Russian Revolution

Two "revolutionary" forces at first collaborated with each other and then clashed: the Communist Party,

1922: Mussolini takes power in Italy

founded by Ch'en Tu-hsiu, and the Kuomintang of Sun Yat-sen. In fact the Kuomintang in this early period followed quite faithfully the directives of the Communists, one of whose major leaders was already Mao Tsetung. This was the heroic epoch of the "Soviet advisors" and of the "Conquerors" described by André Malraux. The death of Sun Yat-sen, on March 12, 1925, marked the beginning of a breach between the two parties which came to a head on April 12, 1927, when Chiang Kai-shek's soldiers massacred workers and trade-unionists in Shanghai (see Malraux's *The Human Condition*).

1927: breach between between Kuomintang and Communists; Shanghai Massacre

From then on Chinese Communism began to take the form it has today. Originally proletarian and directly inspired by Russian ideas, it became military and peasant-centered and gradually detached itself from the Russian model. The hesitations of the Moscow leaders played a large part in the first failure of Chinese Communism in 1927.

China was then ravaged by ten years of civil war, and on top of this came the Japanese invasion. Mao Tsetung's policy in this period consisted of attempts to create *rural* revolutionary cells throughout the country. At first he secured a hold on Central China, especially Kiangsi Province, but he was later forced by the Nationalist armies to move north—and that was the "Long March," beginning in the autumn of 1934 and ending when the Communist leaders decisively installed themselves in the little town

1929: Wall Street crash, followed by the Depression

1934: the Long March

1933: Hitler takes power in Germany

1936: Sian
Incident

of Yenan, to the north of Sian. A key episode in this period is the famous "Sian Incident": in December 1936 Chiang Kai-shek was arrested by the "neutralist" forces of General Chang Hsueh-liang, and freed after the personal intervention of Chou En-lai.

1935: Italy
invades
Abyssinia

1937: Japan
invades
China

On September 22, 1937, the Communists and the Kuomintang began a new attempt at collaboration in the face of their common enemy, Japan, and until 1945 they fought side by side. So much for the theory. In practice, the Communists were busy trying to infiltrate the army and the whole of China; and to a large degree they succeeded, gradually extending their spheres of influence. The Nationalist forces, too, did not always respect their side of the 1937 agreement.

1936–1939:
Spanish
Civil War

1939–1945:
Second
World War
(1941: Pearl
Harbor)

1945: Japan
surrenders to
the Allies

1949:
Chinese
People's
Republic
proclaimed

After the Japanese surrender, fighting broke out between the two Chinese groups. This complex civil war ended on October 1, 1949, with the proclamation of the Chinese People's Republic by Chairman Mao Tse-tung in T'ien An Men Square. The corruption of the Chiang Kai-shek regime had played a large part in its downfall, while another factor in the Communists' victory was the wide sympathy they had gained in rural areas.

1947: India
and Pakistan
become
independent

1948–49:
Berlin airlift

1948: Communist coup
in Prague

The task facing the Communist leaders in October 1949 was vast. Since then, in the space of twenty-two or so years, they have managed to turn China into (as they put it) "a country without which no world problem can be solved."

In the years 1949–52 the regime

established itself. Industry was gradually taken over and a movement for rural cooperatives was launched. The existing structure of society was dismantled. And China took an active part in the Korean War.

1950–53:
Korean War

In 1952 the first Five-Year Plan was launched—with the emphasis on heavy industry, and Soviet aid playing a large part. In 1955, at Bandung, China emerged from her political isolation to "commit" herself on the side of the Afro-Asian countries. Then 1957 was a crucial year, with the ideological thaw known as the period of the "Hundred Flowers" followed by a sharp tightening-up.

1955: China
takes part in
Bandung
Conference

1957: the
"Hundred
Flowers"

In 1958 came the "Great Leap Forward" and the people's communes. The Great Leap meant the harnessing of all available means, technical and above all human—a formidable mobilization of the masses—with the aim of lifting China out of her economic rut. The people's communes are a highly developed form of collective (see pages 40–42), and there were also urban communes. The Great Leap actually led to a vast amount of wastage: the formula of the communes was too radical and had to be revised; there were three bad harvests in a row; and in 1960 the Soviet Union withdrew its aid and its experts. China was on the edge of the abyss.

1958: the
"Great Leap
Forward"

1960: breach
with the
Soviet Union

In 1963 the situation improved. The excesses of the Great Leap were corrected and China made her mark on the international scene.

By the mid-sixties the Republic had

1953:
Dwight D.
Eisenhower
becomes
President;
Stalin dies
1954: France
withdraws
from Indo-
china
1956 Hun-
garian upris-
ing; Suez
Crisis
1957: Treaty
of Rome es-
tablishes
Common
Market
1958:
Charles de
Gaulle re-
turns to
power

c. 1960: be-
ginning of
U.S. involve-
ment in Viet-
nam

1960–1963:
John F.
Kennedy
President
1962: Cuban
missile crisis;
Second
Vatican
Council

PHILOSOPHY AND RELIGION

lasted sixteen years with, at its head, President Liu Shao-chi, Prime Minster Chou En-lai, and, of course, Mao Tse-tung as Chairman of the Communist Party. China seemed to have emerged permanently from her isolation. Then suddenly "the Great Proletarian Cultural Revolution" erupted.

1965–1970: Escalation of Vietnam War

1967: Six-Day War in Middle East

1966–1968: the Cultural Revolution

This "revolution" has been much misrepresented in the rest of the world. It is not easy to explain in a few words, but basically it marked an effort to sweep away the last remaining traces of the old China, and at the same time to reinforce the theme of "permanent revolution" by preventing the Chinese Communist Party from falling into the bureaucratic excesses of "Soviet revisionism." For three years China was in turmoil– Liu Shao-chi and Foreign Minister Chen Yi were both dismissed; China suddenly cut herself off from the world again; and order—a new order, perhaps—was gradually reestablished. Today, Mao remains the guide of the entire people. Chou En-lai is still there. China goes on forever!

1968: May uprising in France; "Prague Spring" and Russian invasion of Czechoslovakia; start of war in Biafra; Richard Nixon elected President

1971: China admitted to the U.N.

1972: Chen Yi dies

Philosophy and religion

In traditional China there were at least four "religions" and a multitude of lesser beliefs, whose mark on the monuments and palaces of Peking is still clearly visible. The most remarkable fact is that these religions developed and coexisted for most of the time in perfect harmony. Clashes between them were rare and an individual could easily be loyal to several religions at once, for there was no incompatibility or exclusivity among them.

The ancient traditional religion. This was the official Chinese religion, its origins lost in prehistory. Heaven created the universe, and the emperor, Son of Heaven, served as intermediary between mankind and the gods. Men worshiped not the sun or moon, but the gods of the sun and moon, and religious practice was intimately bound up with the exercise of power and the double notion of sovereignty and nation. By praying to the supreme gods of this religion one could dominate nature, tame the rivers, bring rain, and enable an entire people to avoid starvation. The Temple of the Heavens, the Temple of Agriculture, and the ancient altars of the Earth, Sun, and Moon still bear witness in Peking to this religion that survived, latterly in a debased version, until the last days of the Kuomintang.

Confucianism. Everyone knows that this is not so much a religion as a public morality. Confucius was born in 551 B.C. He preached respect for moral values, harmony within the State, and the search for truth: nothing could be farther from any notion of metaphysics. What is more, the famous services in the temples dedicated to Confucius, such as the Kung Miao, were more concerned with paying homage to the Master—and following his studies—than with worshiping a demigod, or with the cult of an idol. There was much burning of incense, but this was a sign of respect for Confucius. Like the ancient national religion, the cult of Confucius had a very official character and was even one of the means of government.

Taoism. This is a real religion and is authentically Chinese. At first it too was no more than a system of thought—that of Lao Tzu, a kind of Chinese Diogenes who, according to legend, was born seventy years old. He lived from 570 to 490 B.C. It is said that he met Confucius and that there was a rather unfriendly exchange of words between the two. In fact, however, the morality preached by Lao Tzu complements that preached by Confucius: it is a morality of humility in search of perfect wisdom—"the true way," in a setting of total poverty and solitary inspiration, for the real world is no more than a conventional illusion. Curiously enough, it was this religion of abstinence that most rapidly took on a popular character, acquiring overtones of superstition, witchcraft, and even alchemy. The true spiritual Taoism of a few monks was therefore in contrast with the anarchy of the popular cult. More than any other religion, Taoism has been violently attacked by the

Communist regime, which has destroyed its main headquarters in Peking, the Tung Yueh Temple.

Buddhism. This is the youngest of the Chinese religions and was not really introduced into China before the beginning of modern times. Once there, however, it made rapid progress, its only real rival being Taoism. In some ways Buddhism too became a kind of official religion, the cult not only of Buddha but of certain Chinese-style saints of the Buddhist pantheon, such as Kuan Ti, the god of war, and Kuan Yin, the goddess of mercy, both of whom had many temples dedicated to them. *Lamaism,* the Tibetan version of Buddhism, is also widely represented in Peking. It brings to traditional Buddhism a more formidable quality, embodied in its grimacing "Gods of the Universe" with their necklaces of miniature death's heads. The image of the fat jovial Buddha incarnating the Messiah, or the "Buddha yet to come," in the orthodox Buddhist temples, thus contrasts with the huge somber-faced Prince of the Lamas.

Other religions too have left their traces in Peking. Islam has been practiced since the seventh century, and there is still a vast mosque in the Street of the Cow.

There was also Roman Catholicism, whose famous cathedral of Pei Tang (see general map, D3), near the National Library, was attacked by the Boxers seventy years ago and is today used as a school. The Jesuits, first astronomers and later architects, had considerable influence until they fell out with the more uncompromising Dominicans on questions of ritual. On a decision from Rome that allowed no appeal, the Jesuits' activity came to an end.

Fine Arts

For the uninitiated Chinese, art seems to follow a single unbroken tradition stretching from the red clay pottery of the fourth millennium B.C. to the refined cloisonnés of the end of the Manchu dynasty. But as you get to know more, this simple picture rapidly vanishes—only to return with greater force once you *have* acquired real detailed knowledge.

Architecture. This above all testifies to the remarkable unity of Chinese art. From the oldest surviving documents right down

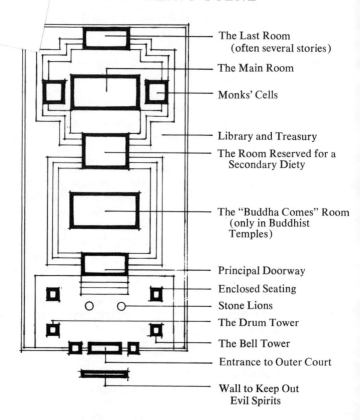

The Last Room
(often several stories)

The Main Room

Monks' Cells

Library and Treasury

The Room Reserved for a
Secondary Diety

The "Buddha Comes" Room
(only in Buddhist
Temples)

Principal Doorway

Enclosed Seating

Stone Lions

The Drum Tower

The Bell Tower

Entrance to Outer Court

Wall to Keep Out
Evil Spirits

Diagram of a Typical Temple

to the end of the last century, all Chinese buildings seem based
on a single model, a plain horizontal box set on a high terrace
of white marble. The roof, with its sculptured timberwork and
painted exterior beams, is the only decorative element. There is
no difference in construction between civil and religious buildings, and temples of every faith are built in the same style. But
within the context of this single style there are several distinct
categories of edifice: the *pai lou*, or portal of honor, made of
marble or glazed ceramic: *gates*, which are in fact palaces,
often of imposing dimensions; *pavilions*, in the gardens or in
the summer palaces, more fanciful in shape or roof decoration;

32

finally, *pagodas,* Buddhist in inspiration, either nine, eleven, or thirteen stories high. The few buildings noticeably different from the above are the *circular temples*, such as the Temple of the Heavens in Peking or constructions of Indian inspiration —pagodas in the form of *stupa*.

Ceramics and porcelain. The first ceramics known in China go back to the fourth millennium B.C., and their resemblance to ancient Greek pottery is unnerving. At first they were black and red, then polychromatic; by the time of the Shang dynasty white pottery began to appear, engraved in imitation of the bronzes of the period. Then under the Han came the first glazed ceramics, as well as masses of funeral statuettes, which were further developed under the T'ang. It is also under the T'ang kings that the first true porcelain made for the imperial court is found. Finally, under the Sung dynasty this porcelain reached its first period of splendor: the loveliest pale greens were used and floral motifs became more and more frequent. This was also the era of the finest household china.

Ming porcelain is justly famous. Numerous workshops turned out goods for Chinese consumption and for export, and the range of products became steadily wider: white porcelain, red and sky-blue monochromes, "three colors," "blue-and-whites." This extraordinary richness continued under the Ch'ing dynasty up to the days of K'ang Hsi and Ch'ien Lung. Painted decoration grew in importance until porcelain was hardly more than a pretext for miniatures and diverse scenes, while *"familles vertes"* and *"familles roses"* flourished.

After Ch'ien Lung the art of Chinese porcelain entered its baroque period. This was a kind of decadence: the decorations became heavier in style, gilding and embellishments destroyed the harmony of line, and the finest vases produced were imitations.

Bronzes. The history of Chinese bronzes begins with the Hsia, but it was under the Shang kings that the finest works were created, uniting sober symbolic decorations with an astonishing vigor of form. Monumental Shang incense-burners, sacrificial vases, and more modest works are perhaps the finest bronzes in the world. The Chou bronzes that followed them had softer contours; the decorative motifs lost their magical purpose and became mere ornaments. During the centuries that followed, Chinese artisans endlessly copied the Shang and Chou creations. The decorative motifs and the variety of shapes became more complex, but to the detriment of classical simplicity. Bronze mirrors, then purely decorative objects, made their appearance. Under the Ming and Ch'ing rulers the art of bronze completely degenerated, and by the end of the Manchu dynasty it had approximated the ostentatious noodle-style beloved by our European grandparents.

Painting. With the exception of a few painted bricks of the Han period and a few scrolls dating back to the "Six Dynasties," very little Chinese painting has come down to us from the pre-T'ang era. Painting was not yet a profession but an intellectual and philosophic amusement. The T'ang period, however, saw the burgeoning of a much richer production, of which there survive the paintings of Tuen Huang (some in the British Museum and the Guimet museum in Paris), as well as the great horses of Han Kan and the delicate landscapes of Wang Wei.

Landscape painting saw a great development in the era of the "Five Dynasties," culminating in the masterpieces of Sung painting. In every way the pictorial art of the Sung period marked the zenith of Chinese painting, but many of the original works of the first Sung epoch have disappeared. The greatest landscape artists were Li Chang, Fan Kuan, Ki Tang, and above all Mi Fei; then, later, Ma Yuan and Hia Kuei with his genuinely lyrical style. We must distinguish the northern Sung painters from those of the southern Sung: they soon formed two different schools and traditions.

The painting of the Yuan period marks a return to realism, but it was under the Ming that the pictorial invaded the world of literature and the intellect. There was almost as much writing about painting as there was painting itself. Technique took the place of inspiration: painting, which had been philosophical, was now often merely decorative. The five most important artists of the time, who took as their models the great masters of the Sung dynasty, were Chen Chou, Tang Ying, Wen Cheng-ming, Kiou Ying, and Tung Chi-chang.

Under the Manchu dynasty the first painters imitated Tung Chi-chang somewhat slavishly, but in the eighteenth century there was a revolt against the excessive intellectual refinement of the Ming heritage, finding expression in the strange individual works of such artists as the monk Kuen Tsan, the great Tao Tsi, and later Li Shan. However, rococo and frankly decadent art remained solidly established around the imperial court. Marvelous little miniatures as well as huge detailed landscapes were produced but inspiration was in short supply and the subjects were always the same. Under the reign of Tzu Hsi, painting became a sort of handicraft.

The greatest twentieth-century Chinese painters are Chi Pai-shih and Ju Peon. Since 1949—and especially since 1966 and the Cultural Revolution—a new style of art has been developed in China to make accessible to the masses what once was the privilege of a tiny minority of intellectuals and men of letters. To propagate the revolutionary ideas of the regime and glorify its leader, Chairman Mao, a complete popular imagery has developed, and today's visitor will come across it everywhere, in the towns and in the countryside.

The basic principle of this new aesthetic is the "socialist realism" borrowed from the Soviet Union, onto which is grafted a mélange of epic style and traditional folklore. The principal forms of the new art are the posters, the popular pictures, the huge frescoes in the largest museums, and also an entire revived handicraft tradition turning out such products as plaster statuettes of Chairman Mao or the happily smiling red-scarved girl Pioneers that decorate vases and woven or embroidered silks.

Language

In China they speak Chinese. That is to say, there's little chance of your being able to understand a single word printed in the newspapers or spoken in the street. There are several spoken languages (Pekingese, Cantonese, Shanghaian, etc.) but only one written language. The northern Chinese do not necessarily understand the southerners, and it is the written language that across the centuries has provided the country with its major unifying force. It is made up of *ideograms*, that is, characters that express not a sound—these vary from region to region—but an *idea*. The ideogram was originally simply a sketch of the object it represented; several sketches together in the same character produced a new idea (for example, woman

+ son = good). The characters have increased and multiplied (you must know about five thousand to read a newspaper, and no Chinese knows the entire range of his language) and the link between the idea and its sketch has loosened. The language, originally monosyllabic, has become polysyllabic by the adding together of groups of ideograms that individually would have no meaning.

A major problem for someone writing about China is how to transcribe Chinese names. There are several systems of transcription adapted to different Western languages, none of them accurate. The best and simplest is certainly that used by the present Chinese government; its only disadvantages are that it needs a special key to be understood and it is not pronounced as it is written. This guide therefore, employs the system most commonly used in the West, the "Wade system." A few liberties have been taken so that the Chinese characters can easily be read—and, what's more, easily pronounced; this will help you on your visits.

THE WAY OF LIFE IN
PEOPLE'S CHINA

Everywhere there are things that are "done" and others that
are "not done"—and in China perhaps more than anywhere.
For the *savoir vivre* of Peking is particularly complex. The
Communist regime has not entirely swept away the long
tradition of Chinese ceremonial it inherited—indeed, far from
it! This ceremonial has even inspired new customs, as in-
scrutably Chinese as anything from the past. The first result
of this combination of old and new is a strange confusion and,
for the foreigner, considerable uncertainty about how to behave. What if he is contravening a respected tradition? Or what
if his conduct proves shocking to the young People's Republic?
Many visitors, educated enough to avoid the crass insensitiv-
ities of some Western tourists abroad, find themselves afflicted
with a curious mixture of guilt and ignorance that may spoil
part of their stay ("Better eat what they give me—perhaps
they're dying of hunger. . . ." "Better not argue—even with the
smiling ones. . . ." "Better not be caught reading *Time* mag-
azine . . ."). And so our hapless tourist lives in a kind of tense
anxiety when really it is so simple to be simple.

Of course there are things it is wiser not to attempt in China.

37

THE PEKING SCENE

For instance, if you leave a tip in a restaurant, they will give you a look of withering scorn and throw back your check at you with a virtuous indignation that is not at all put on. Similarly, it is not advisable to flirt with the female staff— sinister stories are abroad in Peking about journalists who gently pulled the pigtails of a girl elevator operator and had to leave the country within forty-eight hours, charged with "lack of respect to Chinese womanhood." Nor should you joke—or appear to joke—about the taboos of the regime. But Peking has its own line in permissiveness. No eyebrow will be raised if a man appears tieless at an official reception. You may —in fact you're meant to—mess up the tablecloth at an official banquet. You may explore Peking at will, followed perhaps by three hundred inquisitive kids, but sure of your rights since this is an "open city."

But two further words of advice: show yourself to be serious, and at the same time don't let yourself be browbeaten or duped. Both are important.

The tourist *must* be serious, for China's current experience is itself a serious matter and the Chinese all take it terribly seriously. The old Chinese humor has entirely disappeared in the face of the grandeur of the task they have undertaken, and it has yielded to a severe austerity and an incredible degree of morality. So all the noisy, flamboyant, provocative aspects of Western capitalism at play are, in Mao's China, quite out of place and therefore likely to shock the Chinese. And even if you are told—and happily it seems to be true—that after nightfall boy and girl comrades kiss and cuddle in the parks, you should avoid showing too much affection in public for a traveling companion of the opposite sex. Not so long ago the hotel corridors were severely patrolled by the waiters on each floor, and the staff tried to make sure that visitors to each other's rooms would not engage in anything more than decorous conversation in the presence of vigilant chambermaids.

But your own seriousness need not become a devout acceptance of everything that you are so seriously told. It is best to learn to discuss things without getting upset—anger will get you nowhere—and to try to contrast your own very elementary ideas on the monuments that you visit, or on Chinese history in general, with the no less elementary dogmas that will be thrust at you with such a fine assurance.

THE WAY OF LIFE

On a very practical level, you have to learn that a refusal—to give you an air ticket, to let you visit a particular town, to let you into a certain temple—need not have a precise motive, but that it is nonetheless a definite refusal. But if you really want something, don't hesitate to say so, and to repeat your request with your most charming smile. Often you will get satisfaction, especially if you appeal to a level in the hierarchy above the junior one, which must strictly apply the printed rules handed down to it.

On a more ideological level, you will of course be catechized in the Primal Truth and the dogmas of the regime. But if you do have a certain affection for some country (America, for instance) that is generally criticized here, then why not say so, discreetly? Or if a guide gives you details of industrial production or interpretations of history that seem to you sheer fantasy, just let him know what you think. We're sure that he'll be grateful to you!

But never forget that China is a young country that is mobilizing all its energies for a very long-term cause. And don't be upset about this. The Chinese are really very kind.

THE CHINESE AT WORK

In the streets of Peking past and present confront each other on every corner. If you want to take home with you a more than merely superficial impression of the city, you must look both ways, exploring not only the splendid monuments of the ancient past but also the working life of the Chinese today.

For this China of nearly 800 million people is a vast anthill in which each citizen is busily adding his little bit to the construction of a socialist state. An individual contribution may be tiny, but multiplied by 800 million it becomes a powerful joint effort. The Chinese are proud of their China and happy to show it off as their greatest glory: a country the size of a continent, working nonstop to drag itself out of the rut where so many other "developing" countries are still vegetating.

This new China is visible in Peking—the China of peasants, workers, students, soldiers all laboring together at the same task.

The peasants: the people's communes

Eighty percent of China's population is made up of peasants and half of China's national income derives from agriculture, so by any standards the peasantry is important. In addition the peasants are the guinea pigs in a unique Chinese experiment in rural togetherness—the people's communes. Don't leave China without seeing one. If your trip is organized by the China Travel Service, a visit will be suggested as a matter of course. If not, go to one of their offices for information.

The people's communes were set up in 1958 with the aim of grouping together all the activities, urban as well as rural, of the Chinese people. But very soon the urban communes dropped out of the picture, leaving the communes of the countryside to go through a number of transformations. In 1958 the idea was to make them into huge units in which even private life would be collectivized in dormitories, canteens, nursery schools, etc. This, it was hoped, would lead to an agricultural "leap forward," as traditional Chinese structures—above all, the family, considered an obstacle to economic and social progress—lost importance. But in fact the communes soon met opposition, and the Chinese leaders had to back-pedal. Today the collectivist utopia has given way to a very flexible and highly original organization.

There are ninety-six thousand rural communes in China, and each functions on three levels: the commune itself, which is simply an administrative center grouping the most important workshops and other installations; the production brigade, a sort of large village cooperative; and the production team, which decides its affairs with some independence. Major issues such as mechanization or large-scale irrigation are decided at commune level; but the essential unit, the focal organization point of rural life, is the production brigade.

You will be shown this rural life in great detail when you visit a commune. You will learn that the family is still the hub of all activity. Each family has its own dwelling, generally two sparsely furnished rooms, with beds, a table, sometimes a few chairs, and a fireplace or oven; the walls are decorated with a few pictures cut from newspapers, portraits of Chairman Mao, and revolutionary slogans. It is all poor, often very poor, but today's peasants have a sense of security they never had in the old days: they know they can't be driven from their homes by some faraway landlord, and above all they know they will have enough to eat. They feel that they live and work for themselves as well as for China—each family has a little plot of land, a few chickens, maybe a pig.

THE PEKING SCENE

In the morning the grownups go off to work with their teams until evening. During the daytime the children are either looked after by grandparents (who live with the family) or, in most cases, are left by their mothers at a nursery or primary school.

When you visit a people's commune, you will see one or more of these schools for small children. Under the guidance of smiling teachers the children play, learn their lessons, and begin their political education as soon as they can talk. They recite lists of words in unison in high singsong voices, they repeat slogans or count out their multiplication tables. Then they listen to their teachers' tales of revolutionary heroism or purity. Finally, in utter seriousness, they play war games with wooden guns, taking on the imperialists and striking to the ground revisionists and enemies of the people.

Meanwhile their parents are at work. The doctrine of "self-reliance" is the order of the day in the Chinese countryside. This means that each brigade, each commune, tries to provide for all of its own needs, digging canals, manufacturing machines, making tools. Life in the people's communes is a triumph of do-it-yourself handiwork: you'll be proudly shown handmade farmcarts and hydraulic pumps made out of bits of bicycles. But above all you will be shown men and women at work.

The result of all this activity is a production effort that the Cultural Revolution, with all its hazards and uncertainties and the breaks in work rhythm that it caused, did not manage to halt. To get an exact idea of current Chinese agricultural production is not easy, for although there are plenty of partial indications, no complete statistics have been published for ten years. But all estimates by foreign observers suggest a steady increase.

The communes near Peking that you can visit are not altogether typical: if not exactly rich, they are more prosperous than many. The fact that they are always offered as examples to foreign visitors makes one think that they must be exceptional in some way.

An example: the "Commune of Sino-Korean Friendship" (or "Red Star Commune"), ten miles southwest of Peking, groups fifty thousand inhabitants over a cultivated area of twenty-five thousand acres. It has sixty-four tractors, its own repair workshops, mills, an oilpress, and so on. At their disposal the villagers have sixty television sets and there is one radio set per ten people. If you visit the peasants' homes, you will get a real picture of Mao's China, totally devoted to increasing production in a spirit of austerity.

The workers

The workers are the second arm of the "great worker-peasant alliance" that is building the China of tomorrow. They are actually the junior partner, for only 20 percent of China's population lives in the towns; but while you are in Peking they will be your neighbors.

Who are they and how do they live?

To find out, you should visit at least one factory with all its appendages (nursery schools, dormitories, family dwellings, canteens, etc.). In Peking or its immediate suburbs you can go on a complete tour of the "Cotton-weaving Factory Number 3," the "Western Steel Mills," or a large machine-tool factory.

First you will see the workshops: immense factories like any other in the world, save that the machinery is often very old or the product of ingenious do-it-yourself invention. You will be told that China had to solve her own industrial problems after the great "betrayal" by her Soviet friends. Until 1959–60 the Soviet Union provided China—at a considerable price—with major industrial development aid. The Russians sent machines, helped build factories, lent plans and engineers. In 1960, when the Sino-Soviet quarrel began, all this came to an end. The Soviet experts departed, tore up the plans of their future installations, and left half finished the factories they were building. So the Chinese had to continue the task on their own. They set about it as one man.

Hence this fantastic activity of research and technical innovation, this "revolutionarization" of the processes of production—the theme of "self-reliance" cropping up again. Each worker and each team works out the best and simplest ways to increase the productivity of the existing machinery. At the same time they buy new machines singly from abroad, copy the plans, make the machines themselves by hand, and thus complete their half-finished factories.

This overwhelming activity requires a political framework and a spirit of competition that must be carefully kept in trim.

THE PEKING SCENE

So there are incessant workers' meetings and posters of production results on display in every factory. Hence, your guides and interpreters solemnly assure you that only the *Thoughts of Chairman Mao* has enabled the Cotton Factory Number 3 to double its production in the past few years. If this makes you smile, you'll be wrong; for your somewhat dogmatic guide has truth on his side: it *is* because they have worked together in a spirit of enthusiasm and cooperation, carrying out to the letter the slogans sent down to them from on high, that the cotton workers have achieved their results. And although the Cultural Revolution disturbed this movement of industrial reconstruction, its effects today are wearing off.

But there is more to see than workshops. You will also visit the workers' homes. You will certainly note that a whole family living in one room and sharing its kitchen with neighbors marks a state of affairs far below that of the saddest Western industrial suburbs. But here too you must realize that China is building herself up and that the workers' living conditions have greatly improved in the past fifteen years. The workers of Peking do not really spend much time at home: they eat for the most part in canteens; their children spend the day in nursery schools with equipment far more modern than in the people's communes of the countryside; and attached to their factories are playing fields and often simply furnished rooms for rest and recreation.

Unmarried people live in dormitories and the sexes are rigorously separated—less for moral reasons, in fact, than for the more practical one of discouraging the conception of yet more babies to aggravate China's already grave population problem.

The worker has an eight-hour working day—most factories operate three shifts of eight hours each—and one day free a week. He has the right to a few days' holiday a year (three at the Chinese New Year, two or three around the First of October, one on May Day), and if his family lives elsewhere in China, he can get a few extra days to visit them.

He earns little: about 40 yuan ($20) a month. But his needs are simple and his expenses slender: a few yuan for his room, a few fen for his meals. The medical attention from the doctors attached to his factory is free for him and costs very little for his family.

THE CHINESE AT WORK

As well as earning his money, the Chinese worker continues his political education. He attends meetings at which groups of people study the Thought and discuss the writings of Chairman Mao, as well as analyzing "objectively" the situation of their workshop, factory, or neighborhood district. Often the worker will belong to a revolutionary workers' organization and will wear its badge in his buttonhole beside a miniature portrait of the Chairman.

And on his days off he will wander through the streets and parks of his city, taking his family with him. He will smile, eat ices in the street, visit the Forbidden City. . . . You will see him every day.

The Students

The visitor who requests it can, in certain conditions, visit one of the two or three great university establishments of Peking: Peita (Peking University), Tsinghua (the technical university), or the Institute of Foreign Languages. This will be as fascinating and valuable an experience as visiting a commune or factory for anyone who wants to get to know modern China.

But you must first understand the position of students in modern China, in relation to both their earlier studies and to the mass of workers and peasants from whom they have come. School begins in China in the kindergarten, breeding grounds of future Pioneers and Red Guards who sing their way through lessons on war and arithmetic. At age seven the child's real primary schooling begins. It lasts five years, and in this time all children learn to read and write, and they study the rudiments of political history and geography.

Secondary education lasts from age twelve to sixteen (before the Cultural Revolution it lasted for six years), during which time children alternate ordinary study with political education and manual labor. And at the end of this cycle all boys and girls go to "work with their hands" for five years in the fields or in a factory. Only after that may they become university students.

Why this system? Before 1966 there was a national exam that selected students for the universities at the end of their secondary schooling. This exam was abolished in 1966 on the grounds that it favored the children of former bourgeoisie or of State officials and leaders. Since then, students have been selected by "the masses" in the factories or communes where they work, and the choice is then approved by the local Party authorities. It is only after this double recommendation that the university looks at their qualifications. The candidate's level of "political consciousness" plays at least as large a role in the success of his application as his technical knowledge or intellectual training.

In China as elsewhere the university is where new ideas ferment. It was in fact at Peking University that the first disturbances of the Cultural Revolution began in 1966, and there are eyewitness accounts of the extraordinary dramas and humiliations, attacks and counterattacks, poster campaigns and indictments of professors that filled Peita at the time. Professors had fool's caps thrust on their heads, they were insulted, spat at, pelted with mud, and obliged to watch helplessly the destruction of their papers and libraries, before being sent off to be "reformed" in the countryside. The riots at Peking and other universities were at first encouraged, then later disavowed by the authorities; but they reached such a pitch that in some cases groups of workers, and even the army, had to be called in to restore order.

Officially, order returned in 1969. In June and July 1970 new students arrived, the ones already there were sent off to earn their living, and life became more or less normal on China's campuses.

Here are just a few details about Peita. It has at present just under three thousand students, a third of whom are girls. The courses, which took five or six years before the Cultural Revolution, now last two years, compared with three years, apparently, at Tsinghua. Nine students in ten are of modest origin, the rest being the sons and daughters of high Party officials. In Peita there are eighteen departments for literature, philosophy, politics, economics, and law, and eight for science.

A visit to the campus is pleasant as well as fascinating. The buildings are spread around a huge park on the road to the Summer Palace. There are lakes, trees, flowers, and even a few reminders of traditional Chinese architecture. As for student unrest, it has been nonexistent since 1969: after overthrowing the old order, today's students are quietly building tomorrow's order together, it seems.

THE CHINESE AT WORK

What can one think of so short a study cycle and a selection system so very "unacademic" in the Western sense? To condemn it is to fail to take account of China's needs and targets, which are very different from ours. It should not be forgotten that training, especially in science, goes on in factories and offices long after formal studies have ended.

The soldiers

You can't visit a barracks because, unlike the factories and communes, they aren't open to the public and certainly not to foreigners. But the soldiers can be seen everywhere. Take a look at them—they are the cause of prejudices deeply rooted in Western minds.

Seen from the West, China may appear a military state whose vast hordes might one day be unleashed upon Asia, even upon the rest of the world. Photographs and films brought back by innocent tourists have put a lot of emphasis on the Chinese Army, numberless and terrifying. It is true that China lives on a war footing—for the past fifty years she has known nothing but war; she is still surrounded by hostile nations and shots are still being fired in the Formosa Straits. So China is convinced that she must defend herself, never relaxing for a moment the state of permanent mobilization and maintaining her vast professional army of volunteers under rigid discipline.

But the Chinese army is also, and above all, the "People's Liberation Army" whose origins and destiny are linked with the Chinese Communist Party. This army of peasants and laborers was the spearhead of the Revolution. It is this army that made the Long March. It is this army that turned Yenan into an impregnable redoubt and an agricultural fortress. It is this army that brought the regime to power in 1949.

So the Chinese Army has a privileged status and is especially dear to the people and its leaders. It is also closely linked with the nation's economic and social life. It is everywhere—no longer parading menacingly up and down, rifles at the ready, as in the television newsreels, but simply part of everyday life.

If you go for a walk in the countryside, you will see soldiers digging canals, building dikes and reservoirs. In the schools and universities you will hear people say that one must "learn from the army." It is soldiers who are cited as noble examples to the children in the communes and villages—Lei Feng and others who gave their lives for their comrades or for peasants they did not even know. The movies and opera hymn the glory, the courage, and the generosity of the army. You will be told that the army started the Cultural Revolution—and you will know that it was the army that put an end to it! So the army is everywhere.

You have no need to go and visit the army: it will come to you, usually gaily and in good humor, conscious of its importance but always—if we are to believe socialist mythology—ready to render service to the humblest Chinese citizen or to a foreign friend. And it seems that official propaganda here is not far from the truth.

CHINESE CUISINE

It has become a truism that Chinese cooking is the best in the world, along with French. As with all matters gastronomic, this is a question of taste—but at least Chinese food is the most varied in the world. If you visit a selection of the hundreds of Chinese restaurants in London, Paris, or any big American city, you can get an initial impression of this cuisine; but the menus they offer are nothing compared with the remarkable diversity to be found in the restaurants of Peking. There is not *one* but *many* Chinese cuisines.

Just as the geography textbooks divide China sharply into "north" and "south," so are there two totally different styles of nourishment corresponding to this division, each with its own quite separate cuisine. In the south they eat rice and they spice the dishes, for the climate is damp; in the north they eat wheat. The more oily and spicy food of the south goes well with rice, while in the north the food is drier, frequently grilled, and accompanied by all sorts of little cakes, pancakes, and fritters. But this neat division is complicated by a multitude of local traditions, by the distance of the sea, by the climate, and so on.

THE PEKING SCENE

The different cuisines of China

Really genuine Pekingese cooking is little known in the West, where Chinese restaurateurs are mostly from Canton, Shanghai, or Vietnam (save perhaps in San Francisco and New York, where there is a handful of Peking-style restaurants, not all of them authentic). The cuisine of Peking is, however, the most subtle in China. It makes little use of spices and aims at that "symphony of tastes" of which Des Esseintes dreamed in Huysmans' novel *A Rebours*. The most famous dish is of course *Peking duck*, a lacquered crisp-skinned duck cut into small pieces, each eaten, with a spring onion, wrapped in a thin pancake made from flour and dipped in a brown soy sauce. There are hundreds of other Pekingese dishes, such as sea-swallow's-nest soup, shark's-fin soup, shrimp fried in batter, pork in caramel sauce, sugared mandarin fish, grilled duck's liver. There is also a wide variety of snacks in the form of rolls or buns: the famous *paotze*, steamed and with a mince-meat stuffing; *hua chuan*, or spring rolls, fried and stuffed with meat; *yin sze chuan*, little rolls with shining strips of noodle in them that are like silver threads.

Resembling Peking cuisine is that of Shantung, which is also delicate and varied, with a number of delicious specialties such as "aromatic crackling duck," chicken with egg whites and peppers, shrimp fried in batter, sugared sea-swallows' nests, cuttlefish-roe soup, and the traditional sea cucumbers, sometimes known inelegantly as sea slugs.

The second group of styles of cuisine comparable to each other is that of the south and of Shanghai. In Shanghai they eat fish of every sort, including hermit crabs, eels, and shrimp, as well as "Chinese ravioli" (stuffed with mincemeat and boiled), noodles, and fried pork pâtés.

Cantonese cooking is the best-known Chinese cooking in the West, and one of its commonest dishes is fried rice with omelet. (Chop suey is an American-Chinese invention.) They also eat fried noodles with pork or chicken, crisp chicken, sweet-and-sour pork, shrimp and prawns fried in batter, as well as eels and soft turtles. But this rapid inventory of a few of the many Cantonese and Shanghai specialties does not consider the countless ways of adapting and varying them.

While southern cuisine is more spiced than northern, that

of Szechwan or Hunan is even more so. Pimento, red pepper, a mixture of salt and black pepper are staple ingredients. With these they spice some of their famous dishes such as smoked aromatic duck, crisp "Hsiang Fei" chicken (named after a hapless concubine of Ch'ien Lung), chicken with pimentos, and chicken wrapped in lotus leaves and baked in clay. There is also a certain river fish cooked with pimentos and sugar that leaves an unassuageable thirst at the back of the throat.

Finally, the cooking of the traditionally Moslem areas, from Mongolia down to Sinkiang, excludes pork—a meat much eaten in other parts of China. The two commonest Mongolian specialties in Peking are Mongolian hotpot and grilled mutton. Mongolian hotpot is prepared in a huge circular copper stewing pot over a coal fire from which the smoke escapes through a chimney in the middle of the room. The pot is filled with water kept constantly on the boil, and into it are plunged pieces of beef or mutton that are then dipped in a brown mixture of several sauces before being eaten. Mongolian mutton is cut into fine strips and grilled, together with herbs and egg yolk, on a large white-hot iron sheet. In Sinkiang they eat kebabs of mutton, mutton with caramel sauce, and various noodles.

The different Chinese meals

The Chinese eat at least five meals a day: breakfast, lunch, a "snack," dinner, and supper. Not to mention a plate of noodles at ten in the morning or Chinese ravioli at three in the afternoon. These excellent habits have been scarcely modified by today's relatively austere regime.

For breakfast, little cakes, sugared or salted, and a bowl of soup with herbs or noodles in it are served; the breakfast dishes are *ping* (crisp-fried pancakes), *tsin ma hua* (fried strips of cornflour in twisted shapes), *pao tsin* (a kind of very thin pancake), and *chao ping* (cakes made of sesame seed and soybean curd).

At midday there is a light meal, with a little meat or fish and rice noodles.

At 5 p.m. the Chinese eat *paotze* (little steamed buns stuffed with mincemeat) or *tien paotze* (stuffed with jam), or *yin sze chuan* (buns "with silver threads," that is, stuffed with very thin noodles).

Dinner is the main meal of the day. Everyone eats three or four times as much at dinner as during the rest of the day—whether it be a simple meal of cubes of meat with onions, or slices of boiled fish swimming in a clear soup, or else the delights of a full-scale twenty-five-course banquet.

Supper before bedtime consists of a ravioli soup (*huen t'un*), or steamed ravioli (*chung tiao*), or rice cakes (*nien kao*) or corncakes (*yuan hsiao*) filled with jam or sugar, and very sweet. If you take a walk in the streets of Peking, you can easily try a Chinese breakfast or supper—and please note that it was in fact the Chinese, and not Europeans, who first invented ravioli and noodles. But if you want a full Chinese meal, take it at midday or, better, in the evening around 6:30 or 7—they dine early in China.

Drinks

It is a mistake to believe that in Peking only tea is drunk. Certainly it is drunk, but with meals the Chinese generally take beer or wines.

Tea. The commonest kind of Peking tea is jasmine, slightly sharp and highly scented: it is known as *hua ch'a* or *mau li ch'a* ("ch'a"—"tea"—has yielded "char," the British colloquialism for tea).

In the center and south of China they drink a less-aromatic, long-leaf green tea, known as *lung ch'iang* or Hangchow tea. In Canton *hung ch'a*, the tea best known in the West, is drunk.

All tea is served in large glasses—and don't ask for sugar, milk, or lemon, or you will start a new revolution.

Wines and spirits. In Peking the wine most often served with meals is called *hsa hsin* or *huang chin*. This yellowish Shantung rice wine is served hot in tiny cups, and you can drink it without worrying: it contains less than 6 percent alcohol and does wonders to help one to digest the heavier dishes.

At big banquets various white spirits are drunk too, the best known being *mao-t'ai*, made in Kwaichow from sorghum (sugarcane). It is much heavier than rice spirit, but not dangerous.

There are numerous grape wines in China, introduced by the Jesuits, but they are mainly for export and in Peking only foreigners drink them. The red wines are heavy, a bit like Muscatel, and rapidly become boring. The white wines are either rather sweet or very acid and lie heavily on the stomach. There is also a sparkling wine rather like cider that pleases many tourists and costs hardly any more than a bottle of beer. Known under the English name of "sparkling wine" and cool and pleasant, it is initially sweet-tasting but has an underlying bitterness.

Other drinks. Peking beer is excellent, comes in pint-sized flagons, and is served at meals along with the hot yellow rice wine. You can also drink soda water (rather too bubbly and tasting slightly of disinfectant) or an orange soda that is the Chinese equivalent of Coca-Cola—you find it everywhere, always with the same color and taste. There are also some mineral waters, the best known being *laoshan*.

Make-up of a Chinese meal

A meal in China is always eaten at a round table and with chopsticks—you rapidly learn how to use these. Hot towels are brought for you to wipe your hands and face, and then the drinks you have ordered. After this the meal begins.

Eating Chinese-style is an art, and ordering a Chinese meal is no light affair. In some restaurants you can, it is true, sit down at table, glance at the menu, and ask for what you fancy. But if you visit a serious restaurant, the meal must be carefully ordered, preferably in advance.

The meal generally begins with a cold dish—mixed hors d'oeuvres or pickled "hundred-year eggs"—and after this there are probably at least as many dishes as there are diners at the table. A young couple wanting to dine amorously *à deux* must choose between a modest three-dish dinner and a costly one that they will find it hard to eat their way through but that is at least an authentic Chinese meal. The moral: for a good meal, have at least four people; for a feast, a dozen. Chinese cuisine encourages package tours!

If the meal is very long, you can fit in a soup or two between dishes, just to keep up the interest; lunch or dinner *ends* with a soup, for desserts are rare in China and not much to Western taste (except for toffee-apples, which are cooked in boiling water, then plunged into cold water just before being eaten).

meal ends with a bowl of fried rice and eggs, but
of China it would be indelicate to ask for rice
good meal, though it is usually eaten with a simple,
hurried meal.

PRINCIPAL CHINESE DISHES

Hors d'oeuvres (Leng P'an) 凉　　盘

Mixed hors d'oeuvres	*P'ing P'an*	拼
Hundred-year eggs	*Seng Hua*	松
Shredded chicken	*P'an Chi Sse*	拌　鸡
White chicken	*Pai Chang Chi*	白　斩
Shredded offal	*P'an Tu Sse*	拌　肚
Green-bean noodles	*P'an Fen P'i*	拌　粉
Cold duck	*Liang Yatze*	凉　鸭
Duck marinated in wine	*Tzao Ya P'ien*	糟　鸭
Sugared cutlets	*T'ang P'ai Gu*	糖　排
Kidneys	*Yao Hua*	腰　胗
Cold gizzard and liver	*Liang Tchen Kan*	凉　火
Ham	*Hue T'ue*	火

Noodles (Mein) 面　　食

Fried noodles	*Ch'ao Mein*	炒
Cold spiced noodles	*Liang Mein*	凉　辣

Rolls and buns

Buns with silver threads	*Yin Sze Chuan*	银　丝　捲
Spring rolls	*Ch'un Chuan*	春　捲
Wheat-packet soup	*T'ang Pao*	汤　包
Wheat fish (*or* cats' ears)	*Mien Yu* (or *Maoar*) 面　鱼	猫　饨
Sesame cakes	*Chih Ma Chao Ping*	芝麻　烧　饼
Steamed ravioli	*Cheng Tiao*	蒸　饺
Boiled ravioli	*Shue Tiao*	水　子
Stuffed rolls	*Paotze*	包

54

CHINESE CUISINE

Rolls	*Hua Chuan*	花　捲
Fried bread	*Cha Man T'ou*	炸饅头
Grilled bread	*Kao Man T'ou*	烤饅头

Vegetables 蔬　菜

Braised asparagus	*Hue Lu Ssuen* or *Hue Lung Hsu Tz'ai*	烩芦笋 烩龙鬚菜
Bamboo shoots with meat	*Tung Suen Jou Sse*	冬笋肉絲
Leeks	*Chao La Tiao Sse*	炒辣焦絲
French beans	*Chao Pien Tou*	炒扁豆
Peas in sauce	*Hui Wan Tou*	烩豌豆
Peas in chicken oil	*Chi You Wan Tou*	鸡油豌豆
Broad beans in chicken oil	*Chi You Tz'an Tou*	鸡油蚕豆
Tomato omelet	*Fan Tie Chao Tan*	番茄炒蛋
Lettuce	*Wo Suen*	窝苣
Radishes	*Hsiao Hung Luo Pu*	小红蘿卜
Raw mushrooms	*Hui Hsien Mo*	烩鲜蘑

Fish (Yu) 魚

Squirrel fish (boned and cooked in vinegar and sugar)	*Song Shu Yu*	松鼠魚
Fish in vinegar and sugar	*T'ang Hsu Yu*	糖醋魚
Diced fish in vinegar and sugar	*T'ang Hsu Yu Kuai*	糖醋魚塊
Fish with red pepper (from Szechwan)	*Tou Pan Yu*	豆瓣魚
Fish soup (from Hupeh)	*Hue Yu*	烩　魚
Braised fish heads (from Shanghai)	*Hsien Yu Tou*	煎魚头
Sliced fish in wine	*Tzao Liu Yu Pien*	糟溜魚片
Fried mandarin fish in pepper sauce	*Kan Shao Kuei Yu*	干烧桂魚
Mandarin fish in brown sauce	*Hung Shao Kuei Yu*	红烧桂魚

THE PEKING SCENE

Fish with lotus flowers	*Lien Hua Yu*	蓮花魚
Butterfly fish	*Hu Tie Yu*	蝴蝶魚
Fresh abalone with mushrooms	*Mo Kou Su Pao*	蘑菇素爆
Braised sharks' fins	*Hung Shao Yu Chih*	紅燒魚翅
Sharks' fins with chicken and mushrooms	*San Sse Yu Chih*	三鮮魚翅
Sea-swallows' nests	*Yen Wo*	燕窩
Sea cucumbers	*Hai Shen*	海参
Turtle	*Chia Yu* or *Yuan Yu*	甲魚 或元魚
Soft turtle	*Chao Yuan Yu*	燒元魚
Fried eel	*Chao Shan Yu*	炒鱔魚
Eel in sauce	*Hui Shan Yu*	烩鱔魚
Shredded eel	*Chao Shan Yu Sse*	炒鱔魚絲
Shrimp fried in batter (Korean-style)	*Kao Li Hsia Jen*	高力蝦仁
Shrimp	*Chao Hsia Jen*	炒蝦仁
Large shrimp	*Ta Hsia*	大蝦
Large shrimp with caramel	*T'ang Hsia*	糖蝦
Undressed crabs	*P'ang Tsu Hsie*	蒸螃蟹
Crabs' eggs with sauce	*Hui Hsie Huang*	烩蟹黃

Chicken (Chi) 鷄

Chicken with egg white	*Fu Jong Chi*	芙蓉鷄
Chicken with pimentos	*La Tze Chi*	辣子鷄
Three-glass chicken (from Kiangsi)	*San Pei Chi*	三杯鷄
Aromatic crisp chicken	*Hsiang Ssu Chi*	香酥鷄
Crisp chicken (from Szechwan)	*Hsiang Fei Chi*	香妃鷄
Shredded chicken in sauce	*Hui Sheng Chi Sse*	烩生鷄
Chicken with walnuts	*He Tao Chi*	核桃鷄
Spiced chicken	*Tiao Hua Chi*	叫花鷄

56

CHINESE CUISINE

Duck (Ya) 鴨

Peking duck	*Kao Ya*	烤 鴨
Duck marinated in wine	*Tzao Ya*	糟 鴨
Crisp duck with herbs	*Hsiang Ssu Ya*	香酥鴨
Smoked spiced duck (from Shansi)	*Wu Hsiang Hsun Ya*	五香薰鴨
Smoked duck (from Szechwan)	*Hsun Ya*	薰 鴨
Fried Cantonese duck	*Kuantung Shao Ya*	廣東燒鴨
Pieces of boned duck	*Yu Hsiang Ya K'uai*	魚香鴨塊
Fried duck's liver	*Cha Ya Kan*	炸 鴨肝
Duck's liver marinated in wine	*Liu Ya Kan*	糟溜鴨肝

Beef (Niu Jou) 牛 肉

Fillet of beef in oyster sauce	*Hao Yu Niu Jou*	蠔油牛肉
Fried beef	*Chao Niu Jou Sse*	炒牛肉絲
Tendon of beef	*Wei Niu Chin*	煨牛筋

Pork 猪 肉

Minced pork with sesame cakes	*Jou Mo Shao Ping*	肉末燒餅
Pork kidneys	*Chu Yaotze*	猪腰子
Pork balls with shredded cabbage ("lions' heads" from Hupeh)	*Shih Tze To*	獅子头
Pork with rice flour	*Cheng Mi Fen Jou*	蒸米粉肉
Sweet-and-sour pork	*Ku Lao Jou*	古老肉
Pork fillet with walnuts	*He Tao Li Chi*	核桃里脊
Little fried pork balls	*Cha Hsiao Wantze*	炸小丸子
Pork fillet marinated in wine	*Tzao Liu Li Chi*	糟溜里脊
Shredded pork	*Ch'ao Jou Ssu*	炒肉絲
Cooked pork slices	*Pai Jou P'ien*	白肉片

THE PEKING SCENE

Pigs' brains	*Chu Nao*	猪　　朋
Pigs' liver	*Chao Chu Kan*	炒猪肝
Pigs' feet	*Shao Chu Chua*	烧猪爪
Pigs' liver sausages	*Cha Lu Yiar*	炸鹿尾
Pigs' intestines	*Tio Chuan Fei Ch'ang*	九轉肥腸
Pork slices in sauce	*Liu Jou Pien*	溜肉片
Pork fillet fried with egg-white	*Juan Cha Li Chi*	軟炸里脊
Pork kidneys fried with eggwhite	*Juan Cha Yao Hua*	軟炸腰花

Mutton and Lamb (Yang Jou) 羊　肉

Lamb kebabs	*Yang Jou Chuan*	羊肉串
Mutton ravioli, fried	*Kuo Tie*	羊肉鍋貼
Mongolian hotpot	*Shuan Yang Jou*	涮羊肉
Mutton with caramel sauce	*T'ang Hsu Yang Jou*	糖醋羊肉
Grilled mutton	*Kao Yang Jou*	烤羊肉
Fried mutton	*Shao Yang Jou*	烧羊肉
Fried mutton slices	*P'a Yang Jou T'iao*	扒羊肉条
Mutton with sauce	*Pao Yang Jou*	爆羊肉

Soups (T'ang) 湯

White chicken soup	*Chi P'u T'ang*	燜脯湯
Cuttlefish roe soup	*Wu Yu Tan T'ang*	烏魚蛋湯
Three-plant soup	*San Hsien T'ang*	三鮮湯
Chicken noodle soup	*Chi T'ang Mien*	燜湯面
Ravioli soup	*Huen Tun*	餛飩
Szechwan vegetable soup	*Cha T'zai T'ang*	乍菜湯
Egg soup, spiced and vinegary	*Suen La T'ang*	酸辣湯

Cakes and Desserts 点心、甜菜

Chickpea cake	*Wan Tao Huang*	豌豆黃
White-pea cake	*Yun Tao Kao*	云豆糕

58

CHINESE CUISINE

Mooncake	*Fan Mao Yue Ping*	翻 毛 月 餅
Sugared lotus seeds	*Ping T'ang Lientze*	冰 糖 蓮 子
Nut soup	*He Tao Lao*	核 桃 酪
Almond cheese	*Hsing Jen Tou Fu*	杏 仁 豆 腐
Toffee-bananas	*Pa Sse Hsiang Tiao*	拔 絲 香 蕉
Toffee-apples	*Pa Sse Ping Kuo*	拔 絲 苹 果

THE FACE OF PEKING

THE LAYOUT OF THE CITY

Until 1966 all—or nearly all—Peking, old and new, was accessible to foreign visitors. Only a handful of classical buildings that had been turned into offices or State residences (such as the Nan Hai Palace, to the south of Pei Hai) were out of bounds.

Then came the Cultural Revolution. The Red Guards "occupied" the Forbidden City, and many of Peking's palaces and temples were suddenly closed.

Now things are changing once more. In the political thaw that began in 1968–69 decisions taken two years earlier were reversed and the closed doors started to reopen. The thaw has been slowest in the cultural field, however: while many classical buildings are still closed to the public, some have been reopened and others are about to be. In the following pages, therefore, all the main monuments, sites, gardens, and museums that exist are described, because this guide is intended to be as complete as possible and to describe a town that exists, not merely to reflect a temporary situation.

No one can tour Peking if he has not grasped its essential layout, a layout determined by the city's history (see Plan Number 2).

The Districts
of Peking

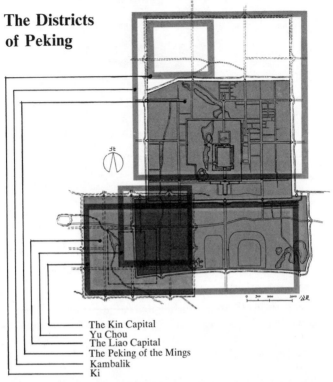

The Kin Capital
Yu Chou
The Liao Capital
The Peking of the Mings
Kambalik
Ki

In the early days there were several capitals here whose names don't matter much. There was Ki, twelve centuries before Christ, whose traces Ch'ien Lung thought he had found and on whose presumed site he erected a monument. After Ki came Yu Chou, built a little farther to the south under the T'ang emperors. Nothing remains of these two towns. And don't trouble to look for traces of Peking earlier than the days of Kubla Khan, for the capitals of the Liao monarchs (tenth to twelfth centuries) and of the Kin (twelfth and thirteenth centuries) were no more than the big towns of little fiefs, entirely destroyed by the invaders who came in successive waves up to the time of the great Mongol.

Kubla Kahn invented Peking. He called it Kambalik, which the Chinese renamed Ta-Tu ("the Great Capital"). Its square precincts went beyond the present walls of Peking on the

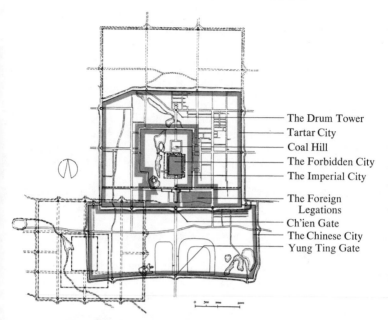

The Drum Tower
Tartar City
Coal Hill
The Forbidden City
The Imperial City

The Foreign Legations
Ch'ien Gate
The Chinese City
Yung Ting Gate

The Main Divisions of Peking (1911)

north side, and on the south they stopped at T'ien An Men Square. Many souvenirs remain of the Peking of Kubla Kahn, such as the Round Tower of Pei Hai and the White Pagoda in the western part of the town, but it was essentially the Ming and Yung Lo kings who gave Peking its present-day shape. Two encircling ramparts gave birth to two juxtaposed cities. The wall of the Tartar City, on the site of the ancient Kambalik from which it gets its name, was completed in 1437. The new city built by the Ming, Chinese City, was not finally surrounded by ramparts until 1464 (see Plan Number 3). These walls, today pulled down, are marked with dotted lines on the map to help you understand the general layout of the town.

In the heart of the Tartar City lies the *Forbidden City* with its high red walls. This was the holy of holies where the Son of the Heavens lived. Around the Forbidden City lay the Imperial City, enclosed by another precinct that has largely

65

disappeared. Here were located the dependencies of the Forbidden City, such as the palaces of Nan Hai and Pei Hai, and the palaces of the royal princes and the highest civil servants of the Empire. In the eastern part of the Imperial City are the big lakes.

The Manchu monarchs built a residence outside the capital, erecting in succession the two Summer Palaces to the west of the town. But within the ramparts they did only some reconstruction along the lines of the plans of the Ming. So Peking was really built by three men: Kubla Khan in the thirteenth century, Yung Lo in the fifteenth century, and Ch'ien Lung in the seventeenth century.

It was in 1860 that the former Legation District was made over to the foreign community, which retained its privileges until the Second World War.

Peking today lies within yesterday's framework but has spread beyond its boundaries. The ramparts, alas, have been entirely pulled down, and all the gates except for Ch'ien Men have been removed, to aid traffic flow. But the ancient part of the city remains. It is pierced from east to west by a very wide avenue, Ch'ang An Chieh, while from north to south there is a wide-open perspective, running from the Towers of the Clock and of the Drum in the north to the former gate of Yung Ting Men in the south, via the Hill of Coal, the Forbidden City, and T'ien An Men Square, the heart of modern Peking. All main streets join these two great axes. These streets are, for the most part, avenues leading from north to south parallel to the Forbidden City, for it is only recently that new east-west thoroughfares have been opened.

PRACTICAL INFORMATION
FOR PEKING

You have just arrived in Peking. If by air, the airport, in the purest neo-Stalinist style, confronts you with its gilt and marble. If by train, the station is huge and deserted. In either case, someone approaches you and utters your name. Don't let this surprise you, even if you have warned no one of your arrival or have—mistakenly—failed to reserve a hotel room. The friendly lady or gentleman coming toward you knows exactly who you are, what your profession is, and why— tourism, business, or journalism—you have come to Peking. He or she has read a little summary of your life history, passed on by the office that issued your visa or by the air or rail service that brought you to Peking. So you must follow this obliging person, who will first take you to your hotel.

The hotels. It is quite likely that you won't be able to choose your own hotel. A room will have been booked for you at one of the two hotels reserved for foreigners, the Peking or the Hsin Chiao, and to one or the other of these you must go. If for some reason you prefer the hotel the Chinese haven't chosen, a diplomatic approach to the China Travel Service might get results. And if you do have a choice in the matter, pick the Hsin Chiao (pronounced Sin Tiao), which is the more central and contains a C.T.S. office.

The two hotels are not of different categories. In their internal organization they are identical. The rooms in both are gloomy and badly furnished, with armchairs re-upholstered in rough cloth and

67

covered with lace head- and armrests, and there are no double beds. The price per day of a room varies from 10 to 14 yuan, whether you are alone or share it with your spouse or with a friend of the same sex. The lighting is feeble, especially in the Peking Hotel. The carpets are threadbare, but there is always a telephone. The plumbing is archaic, but nearly all the rooms have a bathroom—though it is rare for both the shower and the toilet to be working properly. The bath soap with which you are graciously provided is perfectly foul. On the other hand, you get plenty of hand towels and bath towels. The electric current is 220 volts, but there are at least five or six different types of outlet, none corresponding to American or Western European types.

As in most hotels in Communist countries, each floor is a kind of independent entity, managed by the same room-service staff with a bonhomie that is often disconcerting. You collect your bedroom key from the office on your floor and hand it back there, and this office serves as contact with the kitchens as well. You will also find that this floor, like the dining room and other public rooms for the use of foreigners, has kiosks well stocked with free propaganda literature, reviews and brochures in various languages. And you must resign yourself to the fact that the room-service staff know *everything* about your activities.

Service is generally slow. There is a constant language problem, for you can't always have an interpreter with you. But all the staff around you are full of good will and are anxious to understand you even if they can't.

It is quite impossible to get your breakfast served at a precise hour—unless you make an especially strong fuss or can establish a habit over a long period, you may be served up to forty-five minutes sooner or later than you requested. What is more, you must be prepared for a waiter to come into your room without knocking at any hour of the day or night, to bring you a bill to sign or a shirt he has just had ironed. Don't get upset about this: he just won't understand why. But even in Chinese hotels in Hong Kong, where the bedroom doors are flapping Venetian shutters, the staff tend to enter without knocking—apparently it is a general and long-standing Chinese habit. And if you are not alone in your room, you must be all the more alert for such intrusions!

The Peking Hotel. (Ch'ang An, corner of Wan Fu Ching. Tel. 552.231). The former "grand hotel" of Peking is the oldest in the city —and all honor to it. Originally built at the corner of the old Legation District, opposite the French Embassy, it was managed by a Frenchman and more or less represented France. It was badly damaged during the Boxer Rebellion, then rebuilt on its present site at the beginning of this century. The new regime has added several wings and it is now a gigantic building with a very official appeal. Many banquets are held there, in an incredible gilded and over-ornate room right next to the main lobby, itself decorated with immense columns similar to those in the tallest palaces of the Forbidden City.

Young girls in white jackets run the elevators and young men are stationed behind a counter on each floor, ready to hand you your key. The rooms are comfortable and clean. The walls are painted a pale

PRACTICAL INFORMATION

blue. Brown framed twin beds hold oversized feather pillows. The carpeting is in two shades of green and the room furniture is heavily lacquered walnut.

There is a glass covered desk in every room with a bottle of ink, a map of Peking, an English calendar, a stack of postcards, and a bottle of glue for the stamps—alas, there is no glue on the back of the colorful Chinese stamps. Also on the desk you will find a black French-style telephone. There are two buttons on the wall and if you push one of them in the morning a bus boy will arrive with a huge thermos jug of hot water. If you leave a call to be roused in the morning at an appointed hour, the phone will ring precisely at that time and you will hear: "This is the waiter—please wake up."

Bathrooms are half tiled, but they have seen better days. Medicine cabinets hold a new toothbrush, toothpaste, cold cream, hair lotion, and hair spray for American guests. The dining room is large and airy. One eats what is brought to them—and usually quite happily. There are white tablecloths, tea cups in fine porcelain with hand-painted pine trees and silver plate settings along with ivory chopsticks.

The principal attraction of the Peking Hotel is that some bedrooms overlook the Forbidden City. The sunsets are well worth the 2-yuan supplement for these rooms.

The clients are mostly diplomats or other official visitors, some of whom have lived there for months, driven to seek hotel accommodation by the shortage of apartments and even of offices in Peking. The fifth floor has thus achieved a certain fame as a kind of branch of the French Embassy. And because of this quasi-institutional character, the Peking Hotel is not open to everyone: government delegations are put up there more readily than journalists. On the whole the hotel is not much fun since there is neither bar nor lounge, merely a vast dining room where you can order Chinese or European dishes. The rooms (all with twin beds and bathrooms) cost 11 yuan a day facing the courtyard and 13 facing the Forbidden City; two-room suites cost 18 to 22 yuan.

The Hotel Hsin Chiao (*"Hotel of the New Chinese from Overseas"*— Tung Chiao Min Hsian. Tel. 557.731). Set in the heart of the former Legation District, this is in many respects the pleasantest hotel in Peking. Smaller and a little less comfortable than in the Peking Hotel, the rooms are just as gloomily furnished, but they have more daylight. The hotel has two dining rooms: in the basement rather mediocre Chinese food is served, while on the sixth floor the "European" dining room (see page 87) has huge panoramic windows with a view over the whole city. But this hotel has above all the supreme advantage of containing the one and only bar in all Peking. Bar . . . well, of a sort. It is a lugubrious green room, neon-lit, filled mainly by three huge billiard tables much used by visiting Japanese. But there are also five or six tables for drinkers and a real wooden bar. In summer drinks are also served on the terrace.

The foreign journalists in Peking have made it their headquarters, and so it has become a kind of modest "press club" where the rare morsels of information are exchanged. The Chinese government systematically tries to put up at the Hsin Chiao all the writers, journalists, and photographers who come to Peking, as well as most visiting

THE FACE OF PEKING

theater or opera companies. In short, it is a social center for such high society as exists. There are rooms without bath which cost only 9 yuan, while the bigger rooms with bath cost 14 yuan and the small ones 11 yuan.

The China Travel Service

This honorable institution (Luxingshe; general map, C5), the official tourist body, has its head office in the Hsitan Building (corner of Ch'ang An and Hsi Tan. Tel. 667.850). It also has offices in the lobby of the Hsin Chiao Hotel.

Visitor's visa. It is essential to contact the C.T.S. on your arrival in Peking to get a visitor's visa. For to visit Peking itself you need more than a simple entry and exit visa for China: your situation will be considered irregular if you are not officially authorized to live in the city, even if only for forty-eight hours. This formality is important, and without it you may be forced on leaving to stay in Peking an extra twenty-four hours in order to regularize the situation retroactively. It is best simply to do what they ask.

Travel across China. The C.T.S. organizes trips across China, starting from Peking. If you are not a member of a party organized by some special agency, you must go to the C.T.S. in order to travel outside Peking. In fact, being a lone rider is as hard in the rest of China as it is easy in Peking itself.

This book deals only with Peking. There is, however, a *Nagel Guide* in English to the whole of China, written before the Cultural Revolution, and a number of older books as well. Here we shall give only some general details about the kind of trips you can make from Peking.

An individual trip, Peking–Canton–Shanghai–Peking, lasting fourteen days, costs 2,049 yuan in class "luxury A" and 1,464 yuan in class "luxury B." If you travel in a group, you will get better terms, and even a trip for two people allows a discount of 20 percent on the "luxury A" price.

A trip Peking–Nanking–Shanghai–Hangchow–Canton, lasting twenty days, costs 2,663 yuan in class "luxury A," and 1,808 yuan in class "luxury B."

 Sightseeing. The aim of this book is to enable you to visit the town on your own, if you wish. But in some cases you may need to fall back on the C.T.S.—to visit a temple that is closed, or a people's commune, or simply because you need a car to take you to the Great Wall. The C.T.S. supplies cars and a guide/interpreter.

A day's guided tour costs 5 or 6 yuan.

A tour of Peking by car costs about 8 to 10 yuan.

A visit to the Summer Palace and the Western Hills costs about 30 yuan.

A day's excursion to the Great Wall and the Ming Tombs costs 60 yuan.

PRACTICAL INFORMATION

All this is rather expensive, but in many cases you have no choice. So if you are on your own, find a kindred spirit in your hotel and share the costs.

Transport inside Peking. There are buses, electric, buses, and some trams. With a few exceptions they are slow and overcrowded. If you are determined to try them—and the experience is worth it, in its way—take any bus or trolley and go on to the end of the line. The other passengers—from old women down to little kids—will make the touching gesture of offering you their seats, and you'll be cheek by jowl with the Peking masses. But do not attempt to get to any particular destination by bus: it will take you ages, and you may have to change several times. For instance, you need to take three successive buses or trolleys merely to get from the embassy district of San Li Tun to the center of Peking. The only line of real practical use is that to the Summer Palace, which can save you a 10-yuan taxi fare.

Taxis. In Peking there are taxis but no taxi stands—or hardly any. That is, you can find taxis in front of the hotels (except for the Peking Hotel, which is not regarded as a tourist hotel) and at the Ch'ien Men gate. And that's about it. By telephoning—a long and laborious procedure—you can get a taxi in a half hour, but you must state clearly where you want to go. As for the taxis themselves, rattling and swerving about uncertainly, they belong to another age. As an economy measure—for gasoline is scarce—some drivers switch off their engines at red lights, and all of them try to get into top gear at twelve miles an hour. Their engines groan and stall, their upholstery is worn through, but never mind—at an average speed of twenty miles an hour you'll get to your destination.

There are two categories of taxi: those waiting in front of the hotels, which cost 64 fen per mile, and those you can summon by telephone or find at the Ch'ien Men, which cost only 40 and 48 fen per mile. The taxis of this second type, smaller and even older than the first, are often driven by women.

Pedicabs. Many tourists don't dare use the pedicabs (little one- or two-seat buggies drawn by cyclists), but they are an experience. The pedicab drivers are buccaneers who have flown their flag under every regime. Some speak a little English or French, and they're all only too happy to tell you their life story as they pedal along, knowing perfectly well that you won't understand a word. A standard ride, lasting ten minutes maximum, costs a uniform 50 fen—but if you give one of these old crooks a yuan, don't expect any change! Moreover, pedicabs are to be avoided in winter (they are freezing cold, and the driver keeps himself warm but not you) and for long distances in summer (they'll gladly pick you up, but after a half hour in the baking sun you'll begin to regret it). The main advantage of the pedicabs is that you can find them everywhere and they offer a good way of seeing the town.

71

THE FACE OF PEKING

Underground railway. This is due to open sometime in 1972. There will be one line, crossing Peking east to west.

Actually, the Peking subway system has been running for about three years, but it is not yet open to the public. From all reports, however, it is one of the most modern underground transit lines in the world. Long, clean platforms . . . brand new shiny cars. It has been reported that the subway is being operated by members of the Peoples Liberation Army. Cars leave promptly every six minutes, but so far the only riders have been officials and visiting delegations from Communist countries such as Albania, Romania, and North Korea.

Peking not only has an underground railway, but there is now an elaborate network of tunnels that honeycomb the metropolis as a means of escape in atomic attack. There is an entire city complex . . . pipes, coal bins, kitchens, shops loaded with goods, medical stations, and every 10 to 50 feet one can see steps coming down from the street level. Every apartment house and every store seems to have one or two entrances to this brick and concrete tunnel system which stretches for twenty miles out under the countryside. It is an incredible means of escape which was constructed by the People's Liberation Army in their spare time, to be used only in the eventuality of a massive air or nuclear attack.

Maps of Peking

The city council has published a map, but as the Chinese characters on it have not been transcribed, you may not find it very useful. In addition, the Cultural Revolution has left a number of streets with changed names, at least in the city center, even if for many years to come people will still refer to them by their former names. In the maps and plans in this book, especially the general map, both the traditional and the new names have been given for the main streets and the principal *hutung*. The smaller *hutung* are excluded, but all the classical buildings, hotels, and restaurants mentioned in this guide are marked.

 Useful addresses. *China Travel Service* (Luxing-she). Ch'ang An Avenue, near Hsi Tan. Tel. 667. 850. Useful for all problems of hotel reservations, trips and excursions, visits, and so on.

Office of Public Security. 85 Pei Chih Tzu. Tel. 553.102. For entry visas, visitors' visas, residence permits, etc.

Chinese Civil Aviation Company (C.A.A.C). Wu Szu Ta Chieh. Tel. 554.415.

Bank of China (Chung Kuo Yin Hang). 17 Fan Ti Hsi Lou. Open weekdays 9 a.m. to noon and 2 to 4 p.m.

International Club (Kuo Chi Chu Le Pu). 8 Tai Chi Chang. Open from 9 a.m. to 10 p.m.; closed Mondays. Set in the former Legation District, this club, old-fashioned and picturesque, has quite a good restaurant, a bar, a bowling alley, billiard tables, a swimming pool, and, in winter, a skating rink. Only foreigners are allowed in, either as members or guests.

Hairdressers. The large hotels and the apartment buildings reserved for foreigners have hairdressing salons where you can get a haircut or a permanent.

PRACTICAL INFORMATION

Chemists, Drugstores. The most important and central is in Wan Fu Ching.

Doctors. There are no private doctors in China, but the hospitals are excellent and very cheap. In case of need your hotel will make arrangements for you. Foreigners are generally looked after at the Anti-Imperialist Hospital, Wan Fu Ching. Tel. 553.731. Its consultation hours for out-patients are 8:30 a.m. to noon and 2:30 to 6 p.m. You can get vaccinated at the vaccination center on An Ting Men Wai Chiang. Tel. 461.857.

Clothing (see also p. 96). If you arrive in Peking at the onset of winter and are suddenly hit by the cold, or if you have simply forgotten to bring warm clothes, you won't be able to buy cotton goods without ration cards, but woolen and silk goods are on free sale. Ordinary clothing can be bought at the *People's Market* (general map, F3) and at the big *State Shop* (255 Wan Fu Ching). (See chapter on shopping, pp. 88–98).

Photographic equipment. This is much more expensive than elsewhere in the world. You can obtain German film (Agfa) and Japanese (Fuji) on Wan Fu Ching. Chinese film is unreliable.

Post and Telephone. All the big hotels have a post office, and there are also offices in the main apartment buildings reserved for foreigners. Peking's central post office is on Ch'ang An, between T'ien An Men Square and Hsi Tan Avenue.

Price of a stamp for abroad: 52 fen.

To telephone abroad: between 8 a.m. and 9 p.m. dial 334.000, and an English- and French-speaking operator will help you.

FOREIGNERS IN PEKING

For more than fifteen years—not to mention the days of the ancient emperors—Peking has had the reputation of being a city closed to the rest of the human community. A traveler who returns from it is still treated with intense interest. Yet this same traveler's first impression when he arrives in Peking is that he is neither the first to come, nor will be the last. Many Westerners actually live in the Chinese capital, perfectly comfortably; and the businessmen who spend a few months there feel quite at home.

Before you join these foreigners, if only for a few days, you might as well know who they are and how they live.

Until 1949 numerous European businesses were established in Peking, largely in the Legation District. The seizure of power by the Communist Party rapidly drove most of these businesses away, and soon only a few diplomats and journalists were left in Peking. But very quickly foreign students began to flock in, to study at the University of Peking or in its specialized institutes. Then the number of diplomats started to grow, and businessmen doing regular trade with China made their appearance. Finally the first tourists arrived.

Today Peking has diplomatic representatives from forty-eight countries, as well as six or seven hundred foreign students, a few journalists, a few hundred other foreigners settled in the capital—often because of marriage—and more than a hundred businessmen living on a semipermanent basis in the hotels.

Now, with the easing of tension between China and the United States, it is expected that these numbers will increase.

This very small foreign colony does make its presence felt. It is these foreigners who own most of the cars, frequent the smart restaurants, and eagerly go sightseeing in the city. But this colony is very much on the margin of Chinese life, having few contacts with it except purely professional or occasional ones—and the occasions are rare.

The foreign districts. Today the Legations District, with its pink-brick buildings, looks incredibly like a little Belgian or Dutch town sunk in an endless sleep, with no passersby save the uniformed caretakers of often uninhabited houses. Over the years this district has gradually been cleared and the diplomats rehoused outside the city ramparts.

A mile or so to the east of Chien Kuo Men (general map, G5) and to the north of the great avenue leading out of Ch'ang An, the Chinese authorities have built a *second diplomatic quarter*, which is sometimes unkindly referred to as the "diplomatic ghetto." There in a huge building of several hundred apartments (the Wai Chiao Ta Lo) live the diplomats of all the nations officially represented in China, as well as some journalists. Scattered around this building are some twenty embassies, including the British. When the African countries began to recognize China, it was necessary to think even bigger, so three miles to the north of the second one, a *third diplomatic district* has now been built, called San Li Tun ("the village of three *li*"—the *li* being a Chinese measurement). And the embassies—including the French—have sprouted up like mushrooms here, flanked by apartment buildings.

Until 1966 a few rare privileged souls still had the pleasure of living in a real Chinese house, but such people were not numerous, and since the Cultural Revolution, this privilege has ended. All the foreigners in Peking now live outside the town. They have their own shops where you can buy, without special coupons, goods that you can't get elsewhere. And they have their own international club. When they go on a Sunday outing, it is to "do" Wan Fu Ching or to picnic on the Great Wall or at the Ming Tombs.

Westerners in Peking

At this time only Canada, among the North American nations, maintains diplomatic relations with the People's Republic of China. The Canadian Embassy, located at San Li Tun 16, Peking, in the third diplomatic district, has a fullfledged representation, with an Ambassador heading the office, as well as a Consul General who is responsible for the issuance of visas and related matters. The Commercial Counselor may be helpful to those seeking information on business matters.

There is a French Cultural Center with a library, the only Western cultural center in Peking. It is in *Tai Chi Chang San Tiao* (general map, F5), in the former Legation District. Tel. 553.629. Open daily 2.30 to 5 p.m.

THE RESTAURANTS OF PEKING

There must be anywhere from twenty to eighty thousand restaurants in Peking. In every street almost every second or third house has a glass door and behind it two rickety tables, a few bowls, and an oven: it's a restaurant! At any hour of the day—or night—the Chinese are eating. Not being very nourishing, bowls of noodles and ravioli soups are quickly forgotten, and so the eating has to start again. Hence the startling number of restaurants, aimed at rapidly satisfying any kind of appetite.

But the distance between a bowl of ravioli, served with two little steamed buns, and sweet-and-sour sea-swallows' nests is as great as the distance between a bag of popcorn and a specialty of French *haute cuisine*. And very few Peking restaurants have sweet-and-sour sea-swallows' nests on the menu. Most of the city's restaurants are little cookshops, where you certainly eat your fill but where a plate of sweet-and-sour pork or ordinary shrimp fried in batter would be a luxury. It is a fair bet that the cloth-capped customer sitting at one of the tables has never eaten sea-swallows' nests.

There are perhaps only a hundred really distinguished restaurants in Peking, with a menu sufficiently varied and appetizing to merit a visit. The rest at least have the advantage of being all the same: you can go into any of them and know what you're getting in advance.

The information about the restaurants recommended below is, however, incomplete and gives little idea of the extraordinary variety of the menus some of them offer. But these details may offer some help to the more exigent gastronomes.

The serious diner, if he wants a good meal in Peking, must pay no attention to decor or setting: *no* Peking restaurant makes the *slightest* effort to provide a setting worthy of the name. This is not a criticism, merely an observation. Even if the building itself is a marvelous Chinese mansion, the dining room will always have the same roughly upholstered chairs, tables with the same grubby linen cloths, walls lined with the same reproductions of awful paintings. Usually, distinguished guests such as yourselves will be ushered into a small private room, with one round table, a sofa, armchairs covered with coarse cloth, and lighting that is bright and unattractive. Simply console yourself with the thought that it is just like any living room in People's China.

The prices, on the other hand, will bring relief: they are very low. It is hard to define them exactly, for in any given restaurant they may vary up to threefold, depending on the dishes ordered. But don't forget that in a leading restaurant an ordinary dish may serve six or eight people, and that you normally order one dish per diner. The expensive dishes include Peking duck (its price is around 5 yuan a kilo), sharks' fins, sea-swallows' nests, and duck's liver. Other dishes, such as sweet-and-sour pork and nearly all chicken dishes, are much cheaper.

The restaurants recommended have been divided into three categories—arbitrarily, for there is no official classification—and in each case the average price *per person* is stated. In each case these prices refer to very copious meals; it is possible to eat more modestly, with fewer dishes.

THE RESTAURANTS OF PEKING

First class:
One or two diners: 8 to 12 yuan each.
Four to six diners: 6 to 8 yuan each.
Second class:
One or two diners: 4 to 8 yuan each.
Four to six diners: 3 to 8 yuan each.
Third class:
One or two diners: 3 to 6 yuan each.
Four to six diners: 2.5 to 5 yuan each.

Warning: In all these restaurants you can have a meal without bothering about food tickets. In the little cookshops, however, they may serve you without mentioning tickets and then ask for them when they bring your bill. Don't worry: simply make clear to them that you haven't any and they will understand.

It must also be stated that gastronomy is one more domain where the Cultural Revolution has struck heavily. Many restaurants, especially the more luxurious ones, have disappeared. Some were patronized by former leaders of the regime whose fidelity to the dogmas of antirevisionism was severely questioned by the 1966 movement; others were regarded as rendezvous of the "bourgeoisie"; and more generally, the luxury of certain restaurants may have seemed a standing insult to the masses, in the eye of the "purifiers" of the "cultural and proletarian revolution." Despite this, you can still find just about the best Chinese food in the world in Peking.

In the list below those restaurants that are open today or seem about to reopen soon are named first; then the "great" restaurants closed by the revolution—but too good to be omitted—are listed in the hope that they may open again one day.

CUISINE OF NORTHERN CHINA
Peking-style restaurants

The Peking Duck (also known as *Chuan Chu Teh*, "the Reunion of All the Virtues"): First Class. This ancient and honorable establishment has two branches. The main restaurant (Tel. 751.-379) is at Ch'ien Men Ta Chieh, where it crosses Ju Shih Hutung (Number 1 on general map, E6). It has just been entirely modernized: that is, they have rebuilt it, painted the walls white, and lighted it very brightly. The smaller branch (Tel. 553.310) is at Shuai Fu Yuan (the street that leads from Wan Fu Ching

79

to the big Hsie He hospital; (Number 2 on general map, F5) and has kept the style of the old "Europeanized" Chinese restaurants, with softer lights and screens. You can visit its kitchens to see long rows of golden-brown ducks being gently lacquered over low flames.

Of course, it is to eat Peking duck that you go to the Chuan Chu Teh. The duck here is not necessarily the best in town, but it *is* very good. With this as the main dish, don't order too much else. Start with a Chinese hors d'oeuvres (*p'ing p'an*), followed perhaps by a mandarin fish in caramel sauce (*tang tsu kuei yu*) or duck's liver sauté (*cha ya kan*), and finish with delicious toffee-apples (*pa sse ping kuo*).

Pei Hai Restaurant (or *Fang Shan*: the Kitchen of the Empress Tzu Hsi): First Class. Tel. 443.573. Marvelously situated on the Island of Hortensias of the Pei Hai park (Number 3 on general map, D3), this restaurant is worth a visit for its view over the lake and park and for its cooking, which is among the best in Peking. It is also about the most expensive. In addition to all the classic dishes of true northern cuisine (including a fine lacquered duck), it is known for such other specialties as its copious hors d'oeuvres (*p'ing p'an*), its white chicken soup (*chi p'u tang*), its minced pork with sesame-seed cakes (the empress' favorite pastry—*jou mo shao ping*), and all its cakes, some made of chickpeas (*wan tao huang*) and some of white peas (*yun tao kao*).

Pien Yi Fang (*"the Cheap Restaurant"*): Second Class. 7 Hsien Yu Kou, on Ch'ien Men Ta Chieh (Number 5 on general map, E6). Tel. 750.505. An old Manchu restaurant that looks much as it always did. You can visit its kitchens and its oven, which, it is claimed, has been in service for centuries. This is one of the few restaurants in Peking where you can eat lacquered duck without having to order a whole bird: they cut it into pieces at your convenience. Here you can also eat duck marinated in wine (*tzao ya*), pigs' kidneys (*chu yao tze*), and fish in vinegar-and-caramel sauce (*tang hsu yu*).

Restaurants of the Summer Palace (*Ting Li Kuan*). Tel. 281.936. Splendidly situated on the north bank of the principal lake at one of Tzu Hsi's palaces, this restaurant is noted more for its setting than its cooking, which is so-so. At least you have the lake to look at, and the crowds outside before your eyes. Principal dishes: Chinese hors d'oeuvres, skewered meats, various fish. The desserts are good— and that is rare in Peking.

Moslem Restaurant (*Hung Ping Lou*: "the Pavilion of Noted Guests"): First Class. This is on Hsi Ch'ang An, facing the main post office (Number 8 on general map, C5). You walk through several rooms full of diners, as well as empty salons and long corridors, before reaching a private room depressingly similar to all the others in Peking (the "public" rooms are rather more amusing). This restaurant offers everything except pork. Its menu is partly classic Pekingese, partly modified Mongolian. Try the Mongolian hotpot (*shuan yang jou*) and especially the excellent mutton shashlik (*yang jou chuan*). Also recommended is the fried-

THE RESTAURANTS OF PEKING

mutton ravioli (*kuo tie*). The older Pekingese somewhat dislike this restaurant, claiming that its cooking is perfunctory and unrefined—and on the whole they are right.

Shantung restaurants

The Horn of Plenty (*Fung Tse Yuan*), 67 Mei Shih Chieh (Number 9 on general map, D6): First Class. For my money this is the best restaurant in Peking—and thus the best Chinese restaurant in the world. Not to be missed. The cuisine of Shantung, less severe than that of Peking, is perhaps the most refined in China: it combines its own special flavors and the riches of the sea in the greatest variety of dishes you can find anywhere. Try as many dishes as possible—a real banquet—and even so it will cost you less than an ordinary lunch in some pretentious roadhouse outside New York, London, or Paris. It truly needs a poet to do it justice, but here, at random, are some of its best dishes: cuttlefish-roe soup (*wu yu tan t'ang*); braised sharks' fins (*hung shao yu chih*); shrimp fried in batter, Korean-style (*kao li hsia jen*); sea-swallows' nests, either sweet-and-sour or salted (*yen wo*); sea cucumbers (*hai shen*); raw abalone with mushrooms (*kou mo su pao*); duck's liver (*cha ya kan*); braised asparagus (*hue lu ssuen*); and, of course, lacquered duck, the best in Peking (*kao ya*), and crisp aromatic duck (*hsiang ssu ya*). For dessert, the toffee-apples (*pa ssė ping kuo*) are also the best in Peking.

The restaurant's setting and decor are of secondary importance, but they are actually not too bad: after crossing a large silent courtyard, you eat in a classic dining room in the heart of a beautiful one-story Chinese house.

The Restaurant of Harmony (*Tong He Chu*): Second Class. On Kang Wa Shih (Hsi Sze Nan Ta Chieh) (Number 11 on general map, C4). A good restaurant without special character, offering most of the classic Shantung dishes.

CUISINE OF CENTRAL CHINA

Szechwan Restaurants

Since the closing in 1966 of the famous "Szechwan Restaurant" in the Jung Hsien Hutung, there is now only one good Szechwan restaurant in Peking:

Mount Omei Restaurant (E Mei Fan Dien): Second Class. Inside the Western Market of Hsi Tan (Number 15 on general map, C5). The scene in the ground-floor dining room is picturesque: it is full of customers from the covered market, eating bowls of noodles at rickety tables. On the first floor a rather depressing little room is set aside for foreigners. Here you get good spiced Szechwan food. The smoked duck (*hsun ya*) is succulent, as is the chicken with pimentos (*la tze chi*).

Hunan restaurants

Chu Yuan ("the Field Garden"): Second Class. On Hsi Tan Pei Ta Chieh, to the north of Hsi Ch'ang An (Number 17 on general map, C5). Hunan is Chairman Mao's province and people make pilgrimages to it. Its cooking, however, is not remarkable, save that it is very spiced. Chu Yuan is a small, little-known restaurant, where the crisp duck (*hsiang ssu ya*) is good.

CUISINE OF SHANGHAI

Nearly all the really good Shanghai-style restaurants have closed down, notably the famous *Three Tables*. Of those still open, only one is worth noting—the *Yenan*, whose name refers to the street in which it stands, not to its cooking.

Yenan Lou Shih T'ang (*"Yenan Street restaurant"*—formerly called *Yu Hua Tai*, "the Pavilion of Flowers in the Rain"): Third Class. On Hsi Tan Pei Ta Chieh, facing the Western Market (Number 21 on general map, C5). This is not exactly a restaurant, nor is its cooking exactly that of Shanghai. Rather than coming here at ordinary mealtimes, people come for a very late supper or dinner and eat dishes that can be rapidly prepared. The clientele is mainly students and Peking's night-lifers. Try the noodles, of course, and the *paotze*; and try especially the *t'ang pas,* lumps of boiling wheat with soup inside them.

CUISINE OF SOUTHERN CHINA

Cantonese restaurants

Restaurant of the Overseas Chinese (or *Ta Tong Chiu Chia,* "the Great Solidarity"): Second Class. Inside the Hotel of the Overseas Chinese, at the corner of Chu Shih Ta Chieh (Number 25 on general map, F4). This hotel restaurant offers a fine selection of Cantonese cooking. The dining room is huge, beautifully decorated—and a bit solemn. Small private alcoves are shut off with mobile screens. Here you can eat every kind of seafood: shrimp (*chia jen*), langoustines or scampi (*ta chia*), sharks' fins with chicken (*san ssu yu chih*), as well as eels (*sh'an yu*), soft turtles (*chao yuan yu*), crisp chicken (*hsiang ssu chi*), and very good sweet-and-sour pork (*ku kao jo*).

Eng Cheng Chin (*"the Pavilion of Gratitude"*): Second Class. On Nan Ho Yen, almost in the middle of Ch'ang An (Number 26 on general map, E5). This restaurant has just been entirely modernized—it has also changed its address—and its large, clean, well-lighted dining room is one of the best places in Peking for Cantonese food. In addition to the dishes recommended for the Restaurant of the Overseas Chinese (above), try also the "squirrel fish" (*song shu yu*), which is served so well fried and sugared that its bones have melted away. Try also the pork fillet with walnuts (*he tao li chi*) and the beef fillet with oyster sauce (*hao yu niu jou*).

Capital Restaurant (*Shou Tu Fan Chuang*). On Wan Fu Ching. Tel. 422.573. (Number 31 on general map, E2) Formerly the Canton Restaurant. Good food, but nothing special.

Tan Chia Tsai ("the Family Kitchen"): First Class. In the eastern wing of the Peking Hotel

THE RESTAURANTS OF PEKING

(Number 27 on general map, F5). Despite its name, there is nothing familylike about the cooking here: this is a very official luxury restaurant attached to the Peking Hotel. You eat well here as long as you order in advance—and as long as you don't mind the stuffy, old-fashioned atmosphere. You can ask for anything, and it will be perfectly prepared—and expensive. But the quality is not that of the Horn of Plenty.

Wuhsi restaurants

Tong Ch'un Yuan ("the Garden of Spring"): Second Class. 164 Hsuan Wu Men Nei Ta Chieh, at the corner of Hsi Ch'ang An (Number 29 on general map, C5). The cuisine of Wuhsi has no special interest, save for its ways of preparing fish. If you like fish, try the butterfly fish (*hu tie yu*) and the fish with lotus flower (*lien hua yu*). The Wuhsi crisp chicken (*hsiang ssu chi*) is also excellent.

CUISINES OF WESTERN CHINA

Mongol restaurants

The Grilled Mutton ((*Kao Jou Chi*): Second Class. On the east bank of Shi Chai Hai (Number 31 on general map, D2). This used to be one of Peking's most picturesque restaurants, set beside the marvelous Lake of the Ten Monasteries. One seemed to be in another world in this first-floor dining room with its roof open to allow the smoke to escape. Today the place has been rebuilt and is, alas, very modern.

First try one of the two great specialties: the Mongolian hotpot (*chuan yang jou*) or the mutton (or beef) grilled on a cast-iron plate (*kao yang jou*)—a good dish for winter. The mutton shashliks are excellent too, as is the fish in sweet-and-sour vinegar sauce (*tang tzu yu*). Try also the bamboo shoots (*kan hsai shuen*) and, if you are still hungry, the lacquered duck, which is excellent.

Other western cuisines

Sinkiang Restaurant. Second Class. Tel. 890.721. On Erh Li Kou, outside the Tartar City, near the exhibition park (Number 33 on general map, A2). Sinkiang cooking, like Mongolian, is Moslem and no pork is served. This restaurant is quiet, clean, and modern, with no particular character. You can eat good kebabs (*yang jou chuan*), steamed ravioli (*shue tiao*), mutton in caramel sauce (*t'ang hsu yang jou*), and every kind of noodle.

Chinghai Restaurant. Third Class. On Tung Sze Pei Ta Chieh (Hatamen), at the corner of Chu Shih Ta Chieh (Number 34 on general map, F3). The cooking is rather spicy here, but the spring rolls (*ch'un chuan*) are the best in Peking and the mutton kebabs with herbs (*yang jou chuan*) are also good.

RESTAURANTS CLOSED SINCE THE CULTURAL REVOLUTION

Cuisine of Northern China, Peking style

Sha Kuo Chu (or "Restaurant of the Ceramic Cooking-pots"): Second Class. 10 Kang Wa Shih—Hsi Tze (Number 4 on general map, C4). This place is famous in Peking because it offers nothing but pork. There are fifty-seven different pork dishes; and a special set meal

THE FACE OF PEKING

of thirty-two successive dishes, all made up of different parts of the same animal. Try in particular the pigs' feet (*chao chu chua*), pigs' brains (*chu nao*), and the pork fillet fried with eggwhite (*juan cha li chi*).

Yi Chiao Long ("Dragon Restaurant"): Third Class. 21 Ch'ien Men Ta Chieh (Number 6 on general map, E6). A good little restaurant, specializing in different mutton dishes. There are good kebabs (*yang jou chuan*) and fried-mutton ravioli (*kuo tie*).

Tu Yi Chu ("the Friends' Rendezvous"): Third Class. On Ch'ien Men Ta Chieh (Number 7 on general map, E6). Not an authentic Peking-style restaurant. The northern cooking here is mediocre, but there are some good ordinary southern dishes. It is a kind of Chinese snack bar, serving mainly dumplings. These are like large ravioli, either fried or steamed, and stuffed with meat, fish, or vegetables.

Cuisine of Northern China, Shantung style

Tsui Hua Lou ("the Luxurious Rendezvous"): First Class. 70 Pa Mien Chiao, Wan Fu Ta Chieh (Number 10 on general map, F4). The prices are reasonable and the Shantung cooking here is good, if not quite up to the level of the Horn of Plenty. Try the chicken with eggwhite (*fu jong chi*) or the chicken with pimentos (*la tze chi*). The restaurant is also known for its duck's liver marinated in wine (*chao liu ya kan*), its spring rolls (*ch'un chuan*), its extraordinary "three-plant soup" (*san hsien t'ang*) and its silver-thread buns and rolls (*yin sze chuan*).

Spicy cuisine from Central China

Kiangsi Restaurant. Second Class. On Ha Ta Men, near the corner of Wai Chiao Pu Chieh (Number 12 on general map, F5). The cooking of Kiangsi Province is spicier than that of Peking or Shantung. People eat turtles (*chia yu*) and eels (*shan yu*)—and some claim to have eaten dogs (*kao*) too! This restaurant's specialty is "three-glass chicken" (*san pei chi*).

Shansi Restaurant (Tsing Yang Fan Dien—"Tsing Yang" is another name for Shansi Province): First Class. On Hu Fang Chiao (Number 13 on general map, D7). An excellent restaurant in a lovely Chinese house. The cooking is sometimes a bit too oily. The house specialty is a superb smoked and spiced duck (*wu hsiang hsun ya*), while the shrimp in caramel sauce (*t'ang hsia*) is also good, as are the strange cakes called "wheat fish" or "cats' ears" (*mien yu* or *maoar*).

Szechwan restaurants

Szechwan Restaurant. First Class. On Jung Hsien Hutung (Number 14 on general map, C5). The building itself—with its courtyards, discreet gateways, walls "to protect you from evil spirits"—is one of the most genuinely Chinese in Peking. You eat in little side pavilions. The cooking is highly spiced, but you can, if you wish, ask for the dishes not to be too strongly flavoured ("Bu you t'ai la!"). Especially recommended are the smoked duck (*hsun ya*), the crisp chicken (*hsiang fei chi*), the chicken with pimentos (*la tze chi*), and the fish with red pepper (*tou pan yu*).

THE RESTAURANTS OF PEKING

Li Li Shi Tang ("Li Li Restaurant"): Third Class. On Ch'ien Men Ta Chieh, near the Peking Duck (Number 16 on general map, E6). A tiny place, much frequented by the populace of Ch'ien Men Wai. The cooking is genuine and very spicy, and the simplest dishes are the best. The Szechwan noodles (*tan tan mien*) are delicious.

Hunan restaurants

Chi Chen Ke ("the Pavilion of the Universities"): Third Class. Inside the eastern covered market (Number 18 on general map, F4). A small, slightly squalid, but picturesque place inside the covered market best known to foreigners. Here you can eat simple dishes (noodles, etc.) and very good hors d'oeuvres; the other dishes are less notable. This is the only Hunan restaurant in this part of the town.

Hupeh restaurants

Hupeh Restaurant. First Class. On Hu Fant Lu (Number 19 on general map, D7). One of the grandest Peking restaurants—and one of the best, too. This despite the fact that the cuisine of Hupeh Province is a bit hybrid, drawing inspiration indiscriminately from the spicy cuisines of the west, the oily ones of Shanghai, and the drier ones of the north.

The most famous Hupeh dish is called "lions' heads" (*shi tze to*) and consists of shredded cabbage and little balls of pork. It is not, however, the province's best dish—nor are the famous Hankow pancakes stuffed with green beans (*tou pi*) anything to write home about. At this restaurant you would do better to try the fish soup (*hue yu*), the pork with rice flour (*cheng jou*), or the little balls of larded meat with rice (*ho hi chuan*).

Shanghai cuisine

The Three Tables (*Kang Lo—"Comfort"*): Third Class. On Hsin Kai Lu (third *hutung* to the right in Wan Fu Ta Chieh; Number 20 on general map, F4). Despite its name, the Kang Lo is neither comfortable nor sparklingly clean, and it hasn't even got three tables. Yet it is one of the best restaurants in Peking. You go through a tiny courtyard, past a vulgar ornamental stone fountain with eels lazing in the water, to a big dining room where a private alcove has been screened off in one corner, the round table just about fitting inside it. The cuisine at the Three Tables is pan-Chinese—and successfully so, which is rare. Even the Peking duck is good. But the main accent is on Shanghai cooking. Try the hors d'oeuvres (*p'ing p'an*), the hundred-year eggs (*seng hua*), the chicken with walnuts (*he tao chi*), the excellent fried eels (*chao shan yu*), and the best batter-fried shrimp (*kao li hsia jen*) in Peking, as good as that at the Horn of Plenty. Try also the young fried bamboo shoots (*tung suen sze*), and finish with a chicken noodle soup (*chi t'ang mien*).

Wu Fang Chai ("the Pavilion of the Five Perfumes"): Second Class. This is inside the Eastern Market, but you get to it from the first *hutung* to the right in Chin Yu Hutung (Number 22 on general map, F4). It offers some rare specialties of Shanghai cuisine: braised fish heads (*hsien yu tou*), pork-liver sausages (*cha lu yiar*), as well as crabs

THE FACE OF PEKING

(*p'ang tzu hsie*), soft turtles (*chao yuan yu*), and fried eels (*chao shan yu*). Not all these dishes are always successful.

Sen Long ("the Leafy Forest"): Second Class. In Chin Yu Hutung (Number 23 on general map, F4). A good Shanghai restaurant on the first floor of the building. The ravioli soup (*huen tun*), all the noodles, the spring rolls (*ch'un chuan*), and the pastries are excellent. Many European residents of Peking eat here nearly every day.

Lao Tseng Hsing ("Constant Prosperity"): Second Class. In Ch'ien Men Ta Chieh (Number 24 on general map, E6). Another classic Shanghai restaurant, offering every type of noodle and pastry from the Kiangsi Province, as well as such shellfish as shrimp. The ravioli soup (*huen tun*) is very good, as are the fried pork pâtés (*sheng chien pao tze*).

Cantonese cuisine

Hsiao Hsiao Chiu Chia ("the Little Cantonese Restaurant"): Third Class. Inside the Eastern Market (Number 28 on general map, F4). Not especially good or attractive; best for its noodles.

Cuisine of Western China: Mongol restaurants

The Mongol Restaurant (Tung Lai Shun, which really means "the Favorable Winds from the East"): First Class. Inside the Eastern Market, by the Chin Yu Hutung entrance (Number 30 on general map, F4). This is the leading Mongol and Moslem restaurant in Peking, and it also serves very good northern Chinese dishes. There are several dining rooms and two large private rooms on the second floor. It is relatively expensive.

Kao Jou Wan (another "Grilled Mutton"): Second Class. On Hsuan Wu Men Ta Chieh (Number 32 on general map, C5). Mongolian food in a dull setting. When it reopens, it could provide an alternative to the Grilled Mutton at Shi Chai Hai.

HOTEL RESTAURANTS AND FOREIGN CUISINE

You have not come to China to eat fried chicken or hamburgers. If you think you have, you're in for some disappointments. The "foreign" cooking in Peking is bad, really bad, and nothing can be done about it, for it is no one's fault. To succeed with a tournedos Rossini, at least you need tournedos, and these do not seem to exist in Peking. The restaurateurs do what they can to provide Western food, but the results are mediocre—and if you refuse to eat Chinese food, you must content yourself with mere subsistence. Prices are low, however: 2.5 to 5 yuan per person.

Restaurant of the Peking Hotel. This is reserved for the hotel's clients, a pity, for it is the least bad non-Chinese place in town. After five or six months the hotel guests even say they find it excellent—maybe it is a matter of habit. The Chinese cuisine in the same restaurant is quite acceptable.

THE RESTAURANTS OF PEKING

Restaurant of the Hsin Chiao

Hotel. This is open to all foreigners, and here gather all those foreign residents who for some reason don't eat at home. The sixth-floor European restaurant—which offers a splendid view over the Chinese City—has a wide menu, but all the dishes, despite their different names, have the same taste and arrive swimming in one of two sauces, white or brown; the chicken au gratin is quite good, however. The Chinese restaurant—in the basement—is mediocre. The hotel has the best coffee in all Peking.

The Moscow. In the exhibition park. Experts on Russian cuisine would be better able to judge this restaurant, but the food offered here doesn't bear much resemblance to that in good Russian restaurants in major Western cities. However, a large portion of black caviar (a little too salted) is only 2 yuan; the goulash and beef Stroganoff are good, and in summer the salads with cream are refreshing. The coffee is even worse than at the Peking Hotel.

SHOPPING

Shopping. Peking is a splendid town where there is almost nothing to buy. So it seems at first sight, and first impressions are often correct—just ask foreign residents what *they* think! The fact is that the Chinese consumer industry is still in its infancy. Not so long ago (to give but two examples) it was impossible to find in all Peking either face cream or a long-playing record. This heroic epoch has now passed, but even today the shop windows are hardly enticing. Ladies' shoes are depressingly flat-heeled, and an ordinary handkerchief costs as much as a bath towel in any other country. But you don't go to Peking to buy high-heeled shoes, and in shops "reserved for foreign friends" you can buy embroidered silk handkerchiefs for the price of ordinary ones elsewhere. With a bit of care you can find things in Peking that you want to own.

Warning. Before you tour the shops, there are some things to remember. Above all, this is a country where the law—or rather, the public authority—is all-powerful and can use any of its powers at any moment. Note, therefore, that it is strictly forbidden to export from China:

1. Any object, of any kind, more than eighty years old.
2. Any object that the authorities don't wish you to export. There is no precise list of these; one simply knows that certain types of furniture—for instance, those made of genuine rosewood—cannot be exported. For the rest, it is a matter of luck and judgment.

If you have any doubts about the chances of exporting a beautiful blue-and-white vase or even a simple ashtray, you should inquire at the bureau of the Cultural Ministry (7 Liu Bu Keou) that issues

SHOPPING

official export permits. Your visit may be unnecessary, but it is a worthwhile precaution.

Remember, too, that China is a young nation—that is, real antiquities apart, it accords value only to what is new. Hence the high prices of quite ordinary objects, if they are recently made, and the often derisory prices of more valuable objects dating from "before the Liberation." A sword made of marble or semiprecious stone—one of the classic "souvenirs of China"—may cost, if it is new and ugly, three or four times as much as an older sword carved with care and love. This applies to everything from porcelain inkstands to quartz or jade earrings. So you must beware of the appeal of the "souvenir" departments of the huge State stores.

The people of China are friendly toward "foreign comrades" in general and, what's more, they are honest. So you must never haggle over any price—and this is an absolute rule. This is not Hong Kong: no one here will try to cheat you. The prices of everything—down to the tiniest bit of worthless old junk—are fixed uniformly and inflexibly by a "higher" authority, someone far higher up the ladder than the little trader who will sell you a bit of broken jade for a yuan.

How Trade Is Organized in China

In Peking, as in the rest of China, little shops and big stores are organized and run in the following way:

In the beginning was the Word: that is, the *Thoughts of Mao Tse-tung*; that is, the State. All Chinese commerce—or almost all—is closely linked to the State's political organization, when, indeed, it is not part of the State itself. The big stores, bazaars, markets, etc. (for details, see below) belong to the State and are run by it. The same applies to most food stores and to most of the larger shops on main streets.

Some enterprises, such as many restaurants and little shops, are under a kind of joint ownership: the managers have a modest share (from 5 to 15 percent) in the profits. But don't imagine that the sales staff of these shops are more commercial-minded than full State employees: they seem to show the same studied disdain of profit as do the rest of the Chinese people.

Parallel to official commerce, there still exists, however, a small sector that is entirely free. In this sector are itinerant hawkers, old peddlers whose infinitely varied cries used to resound in the *hutung* of Peking and who are not all dead yet. There are also peasants who come to town to sell their vegetables, as well as vendors of fritters and of sweet or salted tidbits—such as the red toffee-apples that little boys patiently line up to buy in every street. You may not do much trade with these merchants, who might be startled to be approached by a foreigner, but who would make a sale with a smile nonetheless.

The Big Stores of Peking

Before you visit the little shops and the "useful addresses," take a look at the four big department stores and markets in Peking—the equivalent of New York's Macy's or London's Selfridge's, with a dash of Paris flea market thrown in. Here you find all that can be bought in China—from cosmetics to antiques, bicycles, and electric motors. Here you should go to see for yourself what the Chinese buy.

THE FACE OF PEKING

The State Shop (Wan Fu Chieng, Pai Huo Talou; see general map, F4). This offers a variety of goods on three floors, and of Peking's big stores it is probably the most "chic" (if that word has any meaning in modern China). If you need any ordinary object, you can probably find it in the State Shop. There may be little choice as to the model, shape, or color, but at least you will be able to get your shaving cream or stationery. The items are not of very good quality or design, and they cost more than in Western Europe, much more than in Hong Kong, more even than in North America—but less than in Moscow. The range of fur caps is especially lavish in winter. But be careful to avoid the counters of pseudoantiques and Chinese handicrafts—most of them are ugly. And before you buy a cake or candy at the food counters, find out, if you can, whether you need food tickets, for the salespeople can be severe about this.

The People's Market (Lung Fu Sze; general map, F3). Very similar to the big State Shop, but instead of being on three floors it spreads out at ground-floor level in what used to be a temple in three buildings rather like warehouses. There are not so many European-style goods here, but an amazing range of bicycles and sewing machines are on display at the far end of a huge hall. Note also the department that sells furs, and especially the antiques department (see below).

The Eastern Market (Wan Fu Ching, facing the State Shop; see general map, F5). This is made up of a network of little passages, rather like the modern shopping arcades of some Western cities. You can wander here for ages, and even get lost. There is lots on sale, but nothing very special (save in a boutique selling modern swords, linen, and various embroideries), and most of the goods are ugly—including some the dreariest postcards you have ever seen. It is worth, however, watching the Pekingese window-shopping—and you should visit the fascinating shop that sells State propaganda posters.

The Western Market (Hsi Tan Pei Ta Chieh; general map, C5). This is less visited than the other market by foreigners, who tend to stick to the eastern parts of Peking near the big hotels. But they would do well to make more use of the Western Market, for it offers the same range of goods as the big stores and is much larger and more picturesque than the Eastern one, which it resembles with its huge covered galleries linked by narrow passages. On Sundays the crowds here are dense, so this is not the best day for doing ordinary shopping. The market includes a second-hand shop with a few old musical instruments at low prices and a lot of metal goods (notably rusty old ice skates). You can also find some little stalls selling silk, and a lot of fritter and cake stalls. But if you are looking for something specific, it is better to try the State Shop.

What To Buy

There are a few things worth buying in Peking: antiques and jewels, Chinese books and paintings, carpets, furs and embroideries, pictures of Mao Tse-tung, and assorted Chinese souvenirs. All these objects are so intriguing that it is worth looking at them even if you don't want to buy.

SHOPPING

Antiques and jewels, paintings and books

Of the antiques on sale to tourists, nothing is really ancient. The rule about "no exports over eighty years old" is rigidly applied, and only a few carefully chosen exceptions are allowed—usually unimportant objects in poor condition, and even for these you need an export certificate. But the salesman will always assure you that what he is trying to sell is exactly eighty years old and no more—and it's up to you to decide whether to believe him.

Needless to say, Chinese objets d'art and knickknacks are far more abundant in China than anywhere else (even Hong Kong), but they are often rather ugly. The following suggestions on where to find the best are the fruit of several months' research in shops large and small.

Porcelain. You can still find in Peking most of the porcelain "families" of old China, but without exception they are copies dating back at most to the last years of the Manchu.

The blue-and-whites are the most beautiful and correspond most closely to the modern Western conception of attractive chinaware. Some foreigners who have not lived long in China may claim to have found real Ming, but it's not true. On the other hand, a very lovely dish made fifty years ago may cost only 2 to 12 yuan, according to its quality; a fine soup tureen should not cost more than 30 yuan, and a nest of four round bowls with a lid need not come to more than 10 yuan. You will find the same in the West for $80 to $100 (twenty times as much). These blue-and-whites are certainly the "best buys" you can find in Peking.

The "*familles roses*" are often very ugly (though there are exceptions), and real antiques are in even shorter supply than blue-and-whites. Small objects are a little more expensive than large ones. Look at the pattern closely: if it is of poor quality, it means the piece has been made very recently and for export. However, a set of small bowls to be used as ashtrays, an inkstand, or a china box make welcome presents back home.

The "*familles jaunes*" can no longer be found—a pity, since they are much admired in the West.

Really fine large porcelain objects are of two kinds, modern and ancient. The first can be found almost anywhere—you can stumble across splendid modern copies of huge antique vases. They might cost up to 300 yuan but about 80 yuan will buy a blue-and-white twenty inches high, which will show to splendid effect in a modern living room. As for older porcelain, it can still be found in Peking, but only under certain conditions. If you are an amateur, get an introduction to the Marco Polo shop (see page 95), where diplomats (and their friends) can buy fine antiques in foreign currency and at the international price. If you are an antique dealer, Peking remains a paradise—not any longer for the finest creations of the best artisans of the Sung and Ming imperial courts, but at least for honest good-quality stuff at lower prices than anywhere else in the world.

Bronzes. It is no use looking in Peking for tiny antique bronzes: you will find nothing of interest earlier than the T'ang. On the other hand it is easy to find faithful copies, with verdigris neatly added as a bonus, at modest prices—say, from 50 to 80 yuan. Perhaps they are wholesaled in bulk by weight.

THE FACE OF PEKING

You can also buy a mass of small objects dating from the last years of the Manchu, the period when Tzu Hsi liked to surround herself with the finest creations of the "noodle style" that later became the rage in Europe and America. It is not very beautiful, nor is it too expensive, and it is still quite fashionable in the West. For 40 yuan you can get a magnificient lampstand or a contorted and not very useful vase.

Sculptures. As with the bronzes, in Peking shops you can find only copies of old Chinese sculptures. A T'ang horse costs 8 to 30 yuan and a stone head 15 to 50 yuan; the stone has the true patina of an antique and stands up to traveling. Copies of the T'ang period, on the other hand, are made of a crumbly plasterlike material and do not travel well: the knights astride most Chinese horse sculptures brought to the West seem to have lost their heads. But a small figurine—a crouching musician, perhaps, or a guardsman—may, if carefully packed up and sent out via Hong Kong and sea mail, finally arrive intact.

Furniture and gilded wood. In Hong Kong you can find new gilded wood objects in every antique dealer's shop window, but there is very little of it in Peking. The gilded wood that, with a bit of luck, you can hunt down, is usually old and not very expensive; it also tends to have lost its gilt. As for real Chinese furniture, it can't be exported. True, you can buy anything that you happen to find in the specialized shops, and most of it is dark wood, heavy and frankly ugly; but the real rosewood, a warm red color, may not be taken out of China. Here and there you will come across superb trapezoid cupboards, or low tables of the kind that were used to enclose big Chinese beds, or charming little cabinets; these will not be expensive, but the dealer will tell you with a sweet smile, "*Wan-wan-li,*" which means "rosewood"—that is, "You can't take it with you." If you are going to spend several years in Peking, buy all you want, and at least while you are there you'll have the pleasure of living amid lovely furniture. But you will have to sell it back when you leave at the price you paid for it.

On the other hand, Peking is full to bursting with curious little jeweled chests and commodes, of all sizes and prices (from 30 to 100 yuan). These are mostly a bit heavy for taking with you by air, but they are attractive and even useful. And they are new enough to avoid the more-than-eighty-year-old ban.

Semiprecious stones. Jade, quartz, agate, amethyst, and so on are very common in Peking, and probably much less expensive than in many other countries. You can buy classic-style figurines in jade or quartz, recently made but of just as good quality as their antique models. It is simply a question of knowing how to choose, for the prices vary (for instance, between 150 and 400 yuan for a Kuan Yin eight inches tall). You can find these stones in all sorts of other forms too, some of them much lighter and simpler: carved plaques, very pretty eggs, snuffboxes, hollowed-out perfume and snuff bottles. A fine incense-burner in what the dealers call "new jade" (that is, it is modern) may cost up to 3,000 yuan, while a mere egg of the same stone could be less than 6 yuan. Just think how much more you would pay in New York or in Europe.

92

SHOPPING

Paintings on glass. Unfortunately there is not much of this left. If you have the great luck to discover—as you might—one of those charming and unsophisticated "Peking beauties" painted on glass at the end of the last century, buy it on the spot. It will be rather fragile to transport, but will look superb in any living room, and will cost no more than 5 to 20 yuan.

Jewels. In Peking you can buy old jewelry or modern old-style jewelry, of all kinds and at reasonable prices. The only jewels not worth buying are pearls, which are very costly in China and so cheap in next-door Hong Kong. Among the best bargains, note the turquoise necklaces and bracelets (from 15 to 100 yuan, depending on the number of rows and the quality of the stones), Mongol jewelry at Marco Polo (see page 95), jade plaques and all the semiprecious stones (see page 92). The loveliest earrings you could find anywhere in the world, in amber mounted on silver, cost only 20 yuan—$8! If you want stones more precious than this, you can find rubies, diamonds, and emeralds, all cheaper than in the West.

Chinese books and paintings. In the eyes of the old-time men of letters, pottery and even sculpture were minor arts because they were utilitarian. A fine Ming vase was the work of an artisan, not an artist. Today, as far as China is concerned, we have a strange tendency to reverse this order of values and to forget that painting and calligraphy were arts *par excellence* in China. What of all this is left in Peking for one to buy? As in other domains, the finest works have disappeared or are not for export. But there are numerous copies on sale, often quite old ones, at reasonable prices.

In painting, the "scrolls" of landscapes or of scenes of public or private life may be up to two hundred years old. A recent copy mounted on silk will cost 5 to 10 yuan. An older copy, of the greatest beauty, may be priced at anything up to 33 yuan. Do not hesitate to unroll several dozen of these scrolls before you find the one you really fall for—some enigmatic portrait, perhaps, or a landscape of gorges and rocks.

Painted books are a good deal cheaper, because of less interest. Almost everywhere you will find volumes bound in silk or wood, opening out like an accordion to reveal a series of landscapes or legendary figures. A small book costs 5 yuan, while a fine work (the best you can find on the ordinary market) will not be more than 60.

Modern engravings, made with antique stones on a special kind of paper, are among the cheapest of "Peking souvenirs": from .50 to 3 yuan. A large black-and-white engraving costs on average 1 yuan. It is worth bringing home a collection, for they look wonderful under glass and matted with rough silk.

Modern Chinese painting is not of much interest. It does, however, stand up to Western criticism rather better than Soviet "socialist realism," simply because its better examples are still steeped in traditionalism. You can find scrolls or modern lithographs at moderate prices, but they are not really worth buying. You would do better to spend your money on the little stitched books that show, page by page, the different phases of the completion of a painting. The "prawn book" or the "frog book" are poetry in images, and cost only 1 yuan apiece.

Calligraphic books are amusing and largely useless. For anything between 3 and 10 yuan you can buy magnificent volumes bound in a semiprecious wood, full of ancient texts with strangely archaic lettering, reproduced by engraving or photography. Some of them are close to our Western abstract art—perhaps the Chinese *did* invent everything! There are also some lovely books of ancient seals.

Materials for painting and sealmaking. The supreme Chinese graphic art is calligraphy, which unites form and content, the poem and its ideal representation. So the true Chinese man of culture had a wide assortment of paintbrushes and paintboxes, bronze inkstands, and pen trays made of single pieces of wood. You can find all these decorative, if not very useful, things at reasonable prices, but be sure to get them from antique shops and not at the stationery counters of big stores.

One of the most amusing curios to bring back with you from Peking is a seal of marble or semiprecious stone carved with your own name in Chinese characters. The carving can be done within a week. Ask the salesman to put your seal in a special embossed case, together with an inkpot full of solid red ink. You could also buy elsewhere an ancient seal and an inkpot (at Liu Li Chang, for instance—see below), and have it reengraved with your name and have a case made for it. Some seals are fine collectors' pieces. You should allow 10 yuan for a seal in ordinary precious stone, and 50 yuan for a fine one four inches high, decorated with carved lions, monkeys, or dragons. Engraving the seal with your "Chinese name" and making the case for it costs about 10 yuan.

The best shops for art, jewelry, books, etc.

Since the Cultural Revolution, things have changed. Till then the antique shops, spread throughout the town, gave tourists a double pleasure: that of buying and that of wandering through the heart of colorful districts that had specialized for centuries in the sale of luxury goods. Thus at the entry to the Chinese City, just beyond the Ch'ien Men gate, there was the Jewelers' Street and the Street of Lanterns. The whole Liu Li Chang district had always been the center for antique dealers in Peking: every day, under the old regime, mandarins and men of letters came here to look for rare vases that the imperial court had not bothered with. Once a year, at the time of the Chinese New Year, there was a famous scrap-iron fair here. All this continued, to some extent, until 1966, but today you will find not a single jewel in the Jewelers' Street, and Liu Li Chang has closed many of its doors.

Here nonetheless is a list of shops where you can still go to savor the last enchantments of a past that is fast vanishing—and maybe also find the lovely ceramic or jade plaque that you are looking for.

19 Liu Li Chang: There are no antiques here. The paintings are reproductions of old ones. But if you want to try your own hand at Chinese painting, you will find all the modern materials you need—inks, paints, paper, brushes.

60 Liu Li Chang: The seals here are a bit too new, but many of the inkpots are antique and attractive.

SHOPPING

63 Liu Li Chang: Without doubt the best shop for original paintings, old and modern. They also sell fine books of calligraphy and some engravings.

80 Liu Li Chang: The only real antique dealer in the street: little low tables, lacquered trays, vases, perfume bottles, as well as lots of other amu̶ useless but pretty.

136 Liu Li Chang̶ can buy the finest e̶ Peking. They also sell copies of antique ceramics—T'ang statuettes and stone heads—and of fine bronzes.

This is all that remains of the former antique dealers' district. In fact, the Chinese government—for reasons of administrative ease and efficiency—is trying in Peking, as it has already done in Shanghai, Nanking, and Canton, to limit to certain fixed addresses the sale of goods reserved for foreign tourists. Thus, besides Liu Li Chang, the Wan Fu Ching district seems to be the most favored for this kind of shopping:

56 Wan Fu Ching: An antique dealer specializing in furniture.

231 Wan Fu Ching: This shop sells all kinds of traditional Chinese musical instruments (these are sold also in the big State Shop in Pai Huo Talou street, see above).

261 Wan Fu Ching: Modern seals and artists' materials.

293 Wan Fu Ching: This second-hand dealer has an indescribable lot of junk, but you might find a masterpiece in its midst.

23 Tunh An Men Ta Chieh: Going northward up Wan Fu Ching, you will find this street on your left. The shop at Number 23 sells the jewels that were formerly sold in the famous Jewelers' Street: necklaces of jade, turquoise, and coral; Mongolian and Tibetan necklaces; amber and agate earrings; jade plaques in the form of brooches; carved ivory. While some of these jewels are antique, most are new, but in an old-fashioned, charming style.

Marco Polo (Mao Long), at 1 Fan Ti Hsi Lou. Open from 9 a.m. to noon and 2 to 5 p.m.; closed Sundays. This is not an ordinary shop and is Peking's only genuine antique dealer. But you must pay exclusively in foreign currency, and for this you need a personal letter of introduction signed by the Chinese Foreign Ministry. This letter is not actually hard to obtain—ask the advice of an embassy or else of the China Travel Service. The Marco Polo's manager speaks English, French, and no doubt other languages. He sells the finest carpets in all China at reasonable prices. He also offers beautiful modern jade and semi-precious stones, as well as fine modern objects in engraved silver (articulated fish encrusted with enamel, bridal tiaras, etc.) and jewels to your heart's content. You can also buy from him (at the international price) some antiques (Ming celadons, small Sung ceramics, etc.).

Carpets

There is a long prestige tradition of Chinese carpets, which are less well known than Persian ones because they are rarer, though often very fine and possibly an acquired taste. In the Peking department

95

THE FACE OF PEKING

stores you will find huge so-called "Tientsin carpets," blue and white or yellow and white, no more interesting than a Wilton moquette. Attractive carpets (old ones from Peking, Sinkiang, Mongolia, and even Turkestan) can be found sometimes in antique or second-hand shops, but often in bad condition. Old carpets in good condition are obtainable today only at the Marco Polo (see above). The lover of carpets—though perhaps not the specialist—can find some good bargains there.

A large carpet (9 x 12) from Tientsin or Peking costs between $350 and $450. Huge carpets from Turkestan, a hundred years old, cost about $800, and smaller ones (6 x 9) around $300. Real traditional Chinese carpets with patterns on a blue background are priced at about $250. Some modern carpets, not very interesting but cheap, can be found at 23 Tung An Men Ta Chieh (general map, F4), and at 17 Langfangtoutiao, between Ta Sha La and the Jewelers' Street.

Furs

There is simply no truth in the widespread rumor that you can get a good mink coat for $200 in Peking. But of course there is mink and mink—and a tatty, poor-quality mink for $200 might not be a bargain.

Fur coats in Peking cost from 40 yuan for a wildcat skin to 450 yuan for a mink. But the minks sometimes turn out to be leopardskins, which are rather different from those sold in the West and do not make very good coats. They do, however, make good coat linings—so in Peking you too will be able to afford to get your ordinary raincoat lined with leopardskin.

The best shops for these furs are:

92 Wan Fu Ching (general map, F5): This has the best choice, and will cut a fur coat, collar, or cuffs to fit you.

10 Ta Sha La (general map, E6): The shop on the first floor also has a full stock. It is a curious ready-to-wear place that looks as if it should have been a luxury store.

19 Tung An Men Ta Chieh (general map, F4): This is the "diplomats' shop," with a good range of furs, especially in winter. The house tailor will fit a coat for you—but you must be accompanied by a diplomat if you want to buy something.

17 Langfangtoutiao: Some good bargains on the first floor.

Fur hats and caps, worn in Peking from November to March, come in all styles and prices, from fake motheaten astrakhan to genuine mink. Oddly, though a mink coat costs 450 yuan, a mink cap may be 750 yuan. Again, there is mink and mink, but for modest budgets there are fine Mongol bonnets in foxskin for only 40 yuan. Here are two addresses for fur caps, but remember that in summer these shops are far less well stocked than in winter:

Ta Sha La (general map, E6): It has hats to fit even the largest heads, which are rare in China.

Here you will find the most sumptuous minks.

State Shop, hat department (see page 90).

SHOPPING

Embroideries

Most of these are reserved for export. They are sent out in vast quantities to Hong Kong, where they fetch ridiculously high prices. In Peking itself only one shop specializes in embroidered linen and handkerchiefs: the second shop (not numbered) on the right in Chin Yu Hutung (general map, F4), coming from Wan Fu Ching. Here you can find cross-stitched table services for six people at 12 yuan, or embroidered organdy at around 16 yuan. A large embroidered white tablecloth, suitable for a table seating twelve people, is 40 yuan. The choice is limited, but the prices must be about the lowest in the world. You can also find some embroidered linen in the jade shop (73 Wan Fu Ching). As for embroidered silks, mandarins' sleeves that can be used as napkins (10 yuan), Chinese jackets (30 yuan), and old Chinese coats of the kind now disappearing (from 25 to 60 yuan), you will find all these at 265 Wan Fu Ching (provisional address of the "Shop of the Minorities").

Modern Porcelain

This is sold in the Peking markets, just as crockery and pottery are sold in our Western chain stores, and much of it is ugly. You can, however, buy "rice-grain" services at fair prices: around 1.30 yuan for a big dish, and .50 yuan for a teacup and saucer. You can also find attractive modern blue-and-white porcelain. Addresses:

99 Ch'ien Men Ta Chieh (general map, E6): This also sells spittoons in the shape of chamber pots.

123 Ch'ien Men Ta Chieh: The largest shop in Peking. *The State Shop* (see page 90). *265 Wan Fu Ching*.

Peking Souvenirs

In this city, as elsewhere in the world, you can find extravagant local "souvenirs" in the most glorious bad taste (the equivalent of all those Empire State Building trinkets in New York). Only a few of these souvenirs are worthwhile and they are extremely cheap. This is where to find them:

Main Store for Regional Chinese Handicrafts, 100 Wan Fu Ching.
23 Tung An Men Ta Chieh: The largest shop specializing in this kind of thing: an incredible lot of junk and some very ugly modern carpets, but also some amusing clay or painted-paper characters from the Peking Opera (about 15 fen), miniature opera masks, some attractive printed fabrics, and all the famous Chinese "paper cutouts."
23 Tung An Men Ta Chieh (general map, F4): Boxes in Chinese silk, small table covers, etc.

In Peking you can also buy all the traditional Chinese musical instruments. The only trouble is that they cost twice as much as in Hong Kong. There are various shops, the best being at 3 Wan Fu Ching (general map, F5).

THE FACE OF PEKING

Basketwork

Chinese basketwork or wickerwork, mainly straw hats, mats, and a few baskets, is not very elegant. If you really insist on buying one of those classic straw hats worn by rickshaw-bearers, you can do so for 1 yuan. The oiled-paper umbrellas are worth buying; they cost 1 to 2 yuan, and are stocked in most big stores. General addresses for souvenirs:

33 Ch'ien Men Ta Chieh (general map, E6).

67 Ch'ien Men Ta Chieh (general map, E6).

255 Wan Fu Ching.
Also the Eastern, Western, and People's Markets (see page 90).

Political Items

If you want to bring home a fair stock of propaganda posters and pictures of Chairman Mao, you must convince the shopkeepers that you treat this as serious shopping—otherwise you risk trouble. We recommend in particular the collections of educational comic strips, and the posters of families pinning smiling portraits of Mao to the walls of their living rooms. A poster costs 15 to 20 fen, and you can find all this kind of thing:

in the Eastern Market, in the main gallery parallel to Wan Fu Ching.

at 32 Wan Fu Ching (general map, F5), in the first room

of the large Jong Pao Chai art shop.

at 16 Ta Sha La (general map, E6).

In all the bookshops you can also find "comics" glorifying the people's communes. In the foreign-language bookshop (7 Wan Fu Ching) you can buy the works of the regime's principal philosophers, printed on India paper and bound in imitation leather, and at the price of paperbacks in the West.

About the only phonograph records you can still buy in Peking are those of revolutionary songs, with "modernized" folklore recordings. You can find them at 25 Wan Fu Ching (general map, F4).

SPORTS

It was a sporting event—a Ping-Pong tournament in 1971, now of historic importance—that helped to reopen the gateway to China. For in China, as in the rest of the world, sports are important.

In Peking, as elsewhere in China, many sports are practiced. In universities, schools, and workers' clubs there are volleyball and basketball courts and areas for other games as well. Teams from different factories play each other, as do teams from the different towns and provinces of China.

But sport in China today has not quite the same significance as in most other countries. It is not merely a physical exercise or a test of skill and strength, or even a means of building a healthy body and team spirit. It is an integral part of an economic and social system whose preeminence must be glorified at all times and in all places.

For this reason sports are part of the general political education of the masses. First of all, the athletes and players themselves feel that they will not reach the height of their sporting potential unless they know intimately and thoroughly the *Thoughts of Mao Tse-tung*. Just as the iron-clad knights would not enter the lists of medieval European tournaments without first throwing themselves into religious or mystical meditation, so today the bright-jerseyed athletes of People's China first read or recite passages from the works of Mao. One example of this real faith was provided in 1965 by a table-tennis champion who explained that he learned his winning game from the four volumes of the *Selected Works of Mao Tse-tung*. Before this study he was but a simple player; after it, he became a world-beater.

Having thus acquired a perfect knowledge of the Chairman's Thought and speeches, the player must integrate himself into a team whose strength and skill are witness to the excellence of the Maoist method. Thus, after first helping to form the individual, sport—and the example it gives—serves to educate the masses. Hence the sporting contests that you can see in Peking—huge, splendid ballets, spectacles designed to stun the onlooker's eye and mind. Every four years Pan-Chinese Games are held in the vast Workers' Stadium east of the City, near the new embassy district (this four-year calendar was somewhat upset by the Cultural Revolution but has now been resumed). These games constitute an extraordinary panorama of colors and flags, and the athlete (the regime's favored kind of sportsman) is, as in ancient Greece, the hero of the day.

Gymnastics in all its forms is Peking's prestige sport. It is the sport that best shows off the beauty of the human body and the force of the ideals that animate it. Gymnasts from all the national minorities arrive from Sinkiang or Kwangsi, from Tibet or from the Peking suburbs, and in front of excited spectators they meet each other in a fine spirit of enthusiasm that has little in common with the Western notion of competition. It is a question less of competing *against* each other than *with* each other, for the greater glory of the regime.

In the international sphere China does not take part in the Olympic Games but she has taken the lead in setting up the "Games of the New Emerging Forces" (GANEFO), a kind of politically committed, leftist Olympiad.

Inside China hardly a day goes by without the press reporting some new national record or victory, or simply the result of some friendly match, played under the debonair and smiling aegis of a huge poster of Mao Tse-tung, mirrored all around the grounds by thousands of miniature posters brandished by the spectators.

SPORTS

Next to gymnastics in importance is swimming, especially since that summer day in 1966 when Chairman Mao swam across the Yangtze. Each summer since then, hundreds of thousands have splashed and paddled in all the rivers and lakes of China, and in Peking in the lake of the Summer Palace. There is also Ping-Pong, of course, and skiing and mountaineering. China has all the sports.

Nevertheless, the foreign visitor who wants to go in for sports during his stay in Peking may be disappointed—for him the facilities are few. There are only a tiny swimming pool, four tennis courts, and one bowling alley—all in the International Club. And in theory you need to be invited by a member of the club—that is by an accredited diplomat or journalist living in Peking.

The Friendship Hotel, on the road to the Summer Palace, has two swimming pools and several tennis courts, but in theory this establishment is reserved for foreigners working in China and for students.

Finally, there are the huge people's swimming pools and sports grounds—including the Workers' Stadium mentioned above—but foreigners are rarely allowed to use them, and generally only as part of official visits.

ARTS AND ENTERTAINMENT

Don't look for emperors and dragons in a Chinese theater: the Communist regime has overthrown not only the social and economic structures of traditional China, but its cultural activities as well. A clean sweep has been made, at least for the moment, and theaters and other shows, as well as sports, newspapers, and music, are now engulfed in the mighty current of socialist education that affects every level of society. Entertainment is a serious business in China.

Traditional entertainments

Peking Opera is a noble art form, with hallowed styles and conventions; let us hope that one day it will be revived. It was born in the days of the T'ang and thereafter grew steadily more complex, but without losing its traditional qualities. Its themes are historical and legendary, dealing with China since the creation of the world, and its heroes are gods and emperors, faithful generals and ferocious brigands. The King of the Monkeys may appear in the same opera as the King of Heaven, a courtesan, and a wicked government official. Long heroic or military sagas are based on a few historical facts; there are long speeches and brief battles—a Peking opera may last more than six hours and, traditionally, is sung only by men. The female roles are taken by light tenors who are the most admired performers in the Chinese theater; the best known of them was the great Mei Lang-fang, who died a few years ago a national hero, thanks to his interpretation of princesses and damsels in distress. The actors in Peking Opera wear no masks, unlike those in the Japanese-Noh Theater. They do, however, wear make-up, and each color has a precise meaning (for example, white faces are those of traitors). As for the tumblers and acrobats so admired in the West, they are only one part of a total entertainment that has many other elements.

In the old days opera in China had a significance very different from that of the theater in the West today. People went to the opera as in another country they might go to a café to round off an evening. The richer ones reserved seats for the whole year, while the poor ones squeezed together at the back in Flemish carnival atmosphere. The vendors of tea, cakes, and fritters fought their way between untidy rows of seats, and some of the audience ordered whole meals from them. The audience hardly listened to the opera—they all knew it by heart anyway, and went there only to enjoy the atmosphere or to wait for some aria that called for a virtuoso performance. When the singer rendered it well, there was a few moments' silence in the hall, quickly shattered by the enthusiastic *"Rao! rao!"* applause of the connoisseurs. And then people got on with their eating.

Other kinds of popular musical theater used to be performed in China—these were to Peking Opera what *opéra-bouffe* or *commedia dell'arte* were to grand opera in Europe. These Chinese light operas were about peasants instead of emperors, and merchants and bourgeois instead of government officials. Each province of classical China had its own form of light opera, and Peking's was *Pin Ch'u*, which used to delight the populace of Ch'ien Men Wai.

The lesser entertainments of Peking ranged from shadow theater (Chinese-style, of course) and storytelling to puppet shows (based on Peking Opera and almost as formal in convention).

Today's entertainments

It had been blowing up for several years and in mid-1963 the storm finally burst: the reform of the theater and opera in China, which swept away all this admirable but "reactionary" folklore. Art now had to be revolutionary, popular, and national. Starting from these three principles, the leaders of China's cultural ideology (or ideological culture) have worked out a doctrine that applies to every form of art in general and to live shows in particular.

This doctrine was, of course, toughened and made more precise during the Cultural Revolution. On the initiative of Chiang Ch'ing (wife of Chairman Mao, ex-actress, who was in charge of cultural matters in that troubled period) a general "purification" of entertainments was carried out. In fact, one of the direct sources for the Cultural Revolution's great debates was a discussion in 1965—an ideological but also aesthetic and literary discussion—about a play that told the story of an upright mandarin who gave up his functions in protest against the tyranny of his rulers. Thus the theater was in at the beginning of the 1966 movement.

Chiang Ch'ing set about eliminating all the elements of "revisionism" and all the traces of "feudalism" that could still be found on either stage or screen. She suppressed all situations that might be considered "doubtful," all ambiguous heroes, all characters who were not manifestly either sympathetic or unsympathetic, leaving only a small number of shows that could be tightly controlled, in a spirit of absolute Manichaeism! "Good" is the Thought of Chairman Mao and all inspired by it; "evil" is everything else—rather like medieval European mystery plays.

This situation may change, but without doubt a page has been turned in the history of Chinese culture.

Theater and opera. The authorities began by sterilizing the traditional Peking Opera, then they stacked all its antiquated scenery and other props in warehouses and double-locked the gates. Every year, on May Day and the First of October, to please "visiting foreign friends," they discreetly take four or five operas out of the cupboard and play each of them for four or five evenings—to packed houses, made up not only of "foreign friends"!

On the corpse of these operas they have erected "Opera on Contemporary Themes," which uses classical music to relate the battles and hardships of the early Communist revolutionaries, the building of People's China, or the struggle of "free peoples against imperialism." Some of these plays are really interesting, while others seem somewhat humorlessly to labor the point. An example often quoted is that of a new opera on the theme of a tussle between man and wife over a pot of "night soil"; the wife wants to give it to the commune to fertilize the people's fields, while the husband, still tainted by the past, wants to keep it for his own lettuces. His wife finally convinces him of the error of his ways, and the contents of the pot, enthroned in the center of the stage, are scattered over the collective pastures.

Each month, sometimes each week, new plays appear that violently attack "the imperialists," caricaturing them as pale and ridiculous figures in the setting of Vietnam, the Congo, Panama, or (formerly) Korea, against a background of rock-and-roll music intercut with shrill flute solos. The "hero" of these plays is less a particular individual than a whole people, a commune, or a battalion. In the theater, at least, they fight against the "cult of the hero."

Light opera has experienced a similar evolution—so much so that it is hard to tell the two genres apart.

Despite their dogmatism, these shows are still remarkably colorful and lively. The acrobatics of classic opera are now armed single combats between Red soldiers and their enemies, or else capers over the barbed wire to free captive patriots. But the style of the movements is unchanged, and so is the music, with its grinding or quivering rhythms, and the gestures, the miming, the grimaces. Behind the naïve bellicose plots with their simple-minded Manichaeism, behind the hideous décors and the boring costumes, there survive in the voices and the gestures the traces of an art a thousand years old—and this is still worth going to see.

Music and Dancing. These have undergone similar reforms, but even more radically for today they ally the old classical Chinese themes (increasingly rare) to grandiloquent Western-style themes clearly inspired by Rachmaninoff or Tchaikovsky. Choral singing of "revolutionary" verses to the glory of Mao ("Mao is our guide") or of Socialism ("Socialism is a lovely thing") is rapidly replacing authentic folksongs and old melodies. The works of Western composers (including the Russians, whom the Chinese imitate) are sharply criticized, and Chinese musicians are called on to renounce "their blind admiration for bourgeois music." The new "classics" of Chinese music are epic three-hour oratorios relating the entire history of the Revolution (*The East Is Red* is the title of one such) in a curious mixture of styles whose sole common ground is that they are sincerely revolutionary. Other new "classics" are descriptive ballets, in which young girl militants dance steps inspired by Marius Petipa (*The Women's Red Platoon*, for instance). At least these entertainments are on a grandiose scale, and this can be fascinating.

The cinema. Popular art *par excellence,* the cinema was the first to take the path of political commitment since followed by opera and music. Today it is only in the film studios of Hong Kong or Singapore that highly colored and emotional fairy tales are produced. In Peking, and in Manchuria and Nanking, only three types of film are made. First, war films (some of high quality, based on episodes in the Korean War or the war against Japan). Second, films that inject political commitment into local folklore—films glorifying the peoples of the "Chinese marches" of Tibet, Mongolia, or Sinkiang, or the "national minorities" of the south. Such films are generally in color, with naïve plots set against splendid landscapes; the masterpiece of this kind is *The Stag*, the story of a Tibetan peasant in the years before the democratic reform of 1959. Third, there are films about the people's communes, or factory workers, or good little housewives, or obedient young boys, or generous sons-in-law—a whole new mythology that is usually pretty dull. There are also some famous puppet films, few in number but well directed, and some good documentaries.

As for foreign films, there are almost none to be seen in Peking, save in the foreign embassies. Sometimes an Albanian film appears or, more frequently one from North Korea, but these are rarely worth seeing. Russian films are considered "revisionist." A French film once played to full houses in a cinema on Ta Sha La: it was called *Tamango*—and who has ever heard of it?

The Peking Circus. Even the circus has been forced to toe the line, but since circus performances are mainly a matter of physical techniques, it has suffered less change than other entertainments. The Peking Circus is an amazing mixture of jugglers, acrobats, and conjurors who follow each other in bevies, interrupted from time to time by a group of clowns. The show is often of some quality, especially the acrobats who, incredibly light and agile, climb their way up to the ceilings on piles of chairs, juggling plates as they go. And the conjurors good-humoredly extricate double-doored wardrobes from the clothes of little red-scarved Pioneers. But the clowns have been politicized—that is to say, they are ridiculous Uncle Sams or grotesque GIs who flee, leaving their trousers behind, when confronted by fierce Chinese virgins.

Unfortunately, the Peking Circus rarely gives performances there: its company, one of the best in the world, is nearly always away on tour.

Reserving tickets for shows. Going to a show in Peking is the easiest thing in the world. The Chinese Tourist Office is fairly proud of national productions and will find you seats for any theater or cinema performance. Prices range from 60 fen to 1 yuan—on this level, at least, the Chinese theater is a success: the prices are truly popular.

It is worth seeing at least one opera "on a contemporary theme" as well as a big modern ballet or an oratorio of *The East Is Red* type, if one is being performed. Go and see a film or two as well, less for the film itself than for the audience, which reacts with tireless enthusiasm to the long tirades of which, presumably, you won't follow a word. The theater public is even more colorful, and you may find yourself sitting beside a soldier in uniform or an old grandmother with a pipe between her teeth.

On the other hand, you can safely stay away from the so-called "folklore" entertainments, which now are merely tedious displays in which only the costumes of the dancers are authentic.

Traditional festivals. In old China there were almost as many festivals as days in the calendar. The seventh day of the first month was the festival of all human beings, the eighth day of the first month that of homage due to the stars, and so on till New Year's Day, when it all began again. Each festival had its own special rites: a fair in a temple, horse races, masked balls, lanterns, specially made cakes and sweets known as "mooncakes," "flour fish," "dragons," etc. If you leave China via Hong Kong or Macao, you can still perhaps see the spectacle of the dragon boats, the festival of the moon, or "the day one climbs the mountain." An interesting book edited by Derk Bodde, *Annual Customs and Festivals in Peking*, gives a more or less complete calendar of these festivities.

But the Communist regime has put a stop to all this. Two strong lines of argument were used simultaneously against the festivals: they were relics of feudal superstition and they were a useless waste of money. These apparently won the day, and if you go for a walk in Peking on a major festival, the streets seem the same as on any other day. But since the Chinese press continues to mount its attacks on people who observe outdated practices, it is pretty safe to conclude that behind closed doors the traditional festivals go on.

The Chinese New Year is still celebrated with a certain amount of pomp, but it is only a shadow of what it was. One month before the date—it falls generally in February—the press warns the people not to throw their money away; and whereas in former days a huge fair was held at Liu Li Chang, today this has been replaced by "sales centers" that turn a few streetcorners into modest carnivals. At Tung Sze, in front of the People's Market (general map, F3), and on Ch'ang An, between Ha Ta Men and Wan Fu Ching (F5), the stalls are numerous enough to make a picturesque scene: they sell paper dragons, tiny flags, multicolored pinwheels, and rattles. It's a long, long way from the stupefying pandemonium of the New Year in Hong Kong.

National festivals. In place of the traditional holidays are the magnificent "revolutionary" festivals of the new regime. If you can arrange your stay in Peking to coincide with May Day or the First of October, you can take part in the most extraordinary crowd scenes to be seen anywhere. The National Chinese Festival (October 1) is perhaps a little more impressive than May Day, but both have the same general style.

For more than a month on both occasions, hundreds of thousands of men and women practice a two-hour procession, in the morning, in front of the T'ien An Men gate. On the great day Mao Tse-tung stands on the platform of honor set up at the gate, and there, surrounded by his distinguished guests, he takes part in the ceremony. Decorated carriages, folklore groups, popular militia jogtrot past the Chinese leaders with cries of "Long live Chairman Mao!" They brandish paper flowers, while carnival music blares and volleys of balloons and doves are released above them.

In the evening the square and the imperial palaces are lit up with fireworks—the best place from which to watch this is the terrace of the Peking Hotel—and then groups form in the T'ien An Men Square for country dances and folk dances. All this is well organized—perhaps *too* well, for one feels that nothing has been left to chance in all the coming and going of peasants in regional costume and soldiers of the People's Liberation Army. But gaiety and good humor reign, and the circles of dancers will open to allow you to pass to the very front.

Demonstrations. There are other festivals, also official, but their dates vary according to the visits of leaders of friendly countries or the timing of the aggressive acts of American imperialism. All are picturesque. For the official visits thousands of boys and girls wave little flags and march past singing. In the anti-imperialist mass demonstrations, groups walk up and down the principal streets of Peking for three days and three evenings, brandishing vengeful slogans and red flags in a happy carnival atmosphere. There are little improvised scenes on the T'ien An Men Square, where you see grotesque Uncle Sams all in chains, with their long noses and high tophats, or very pretty young girl soldiers bellowing out anthems composed within the past forty-eight hours. Two or three hundred thousand people shout, together or separately, their hatred of imperialism, clearly delighted to have an excuse for escaping from school, office, or factory. And if you want to take photographs, you can do so without a thought: you will even be encouraged, for at such demonstrations China speaks to the world, and you can help carry the message.

The View from the Top of the Hill of Coal

The travel agencies and the older inhabitants of Peking generally advise you to begin your visit by climbing to the top of the *Hill of Coal*. This is an excellent idea, as long as you don't do it at noon, when the sun, full in the south, dazzles the poor visitor, who can see nothing at all. In the early morning or at the end of the afternoon, and particularly at sunset, the view is magnificient.

The Hill of Coal (Mei Shan), or "Hill of Contemplation," was built by Yung Lo, probably on the site of a former coal-pile. It is an artificial mountain whose purpose was to protect the imperial palaces from both the winds and the evil spirits coming from the north. It quickly became a favorite spot for walks and excursions, and the eunuchs and the ladies of the seraglio would recite poetry there at sunset while contemplating the marvelous landscape of towers and lakes. There it was in 1644 that the last of the Ming emperors, Ch'ung Cheng, hanged himself from a juniper tree. On the slope of the hill Ch'ien Lung built five symmetrically tiered pavilions whose fame spread even to Russia: Catherine the Great copied them in her part of Tsarkoe Selo.

From the top of the hill the whole town is spread before your eyes. To the north, beyond the former Palace of Imperial Longevity (Shou Huang Tien) built by Ch'ien Lung, which lies just at the foot of the hill and used to house the portraits of the Manchu emperors, you can see the Tower of the Clock and the Tower of the Drum. It was the sound of instruments hidden in these massive constructions that in the olden days regulated the working hours of the imperial civil servants.

To the west the view stretches over the parks and lakes of the city: Nan Hai, Chung Hai, and Pei Hai (the lakes of the south, center, and north—"hai" means lake). At the edge of Pei Hai lies the famous "Bottle of Peppermint," the White Dagoba.

To the east, factories have made huge blemishes in the marvelous checkerboard of the houses of Peking—gray houses with gray roofs and courtyards overflowing with trees and flowers, between the hutung so verdant in summer, so arid in winter.

But above all, it is to the south that you must look. There the master plan of the imperial palaces is displayed in all its splendor. The geography of the Forbidden City becomes apparent: a long rectangle bordered with high walls, extraordinary angular towers with complicated roofs suspended above the moats, and, in the middle, the City. Look at it closely: no one before the revolution of 1911 had the right to enjoy this view unless he was an official guest of the Court. The central palaces with their varnished yellow roofs rise one upon the other like waves. To left and right the wings reserved for the concubines and empresses form a maze of courtyards and corridors, their profusion contrasting with the splendid simplicity of the main buildings. Farther off, beyond T'ien An Men, stands the great triumphal gate of Ch'ien Men which closes the Tartar City on its southern side; and far on the horizon, slightly to the east, are the roofs of the Temple of Heaven.

Go down again from the Hill of Coal. It is time to penetrate the holy of holies. You must be in a state of grace.

(NOTE: Photography enthusiasts should be warned that because of Peking's high luminosity and the lack of light-and-shade relief it is hard to take satisfactory pictures. Try to use an ultraviolet filter.)

THE FORBIDDEN CITY

If you have no more than half a day to spend in Peking, clearly the Forbidden City must take priority. Not that you get to know it in two hours, but at least you can come away with an impression of incredible grandeur that is found nowhere else on earth. Versailles is fine, the Vatican and the Kremlin are imposing, Niagara or the Grand Canyon may take your breath away; but the Forbidden City of Peking, beautiful and imposing, is the world's most perfect example of a gigantic edifice harmonious in its mixture of simplicity and diversity.

It was first built by the Ming sovereign, Yung Lo (1403–24). Over the years the palaces burned down or crumbled away, and Ch'ien Lung (1736–96) rebuilt the City almost entirely, adding new palaces to it. Finally Tzu Hsi put up various pavilions in the northern part of the precincts. The remarkable harmony of the construction results from the extreme simplicity of Chinese architecture. Nearly all the buildings are of only two stories, and are aligned around courtyards whose proportions vary with the importance of the palaces they serve. Nowhere more than in the Forbidden City is detail better subordinated to an overall harmony. Hence this impression of serene majesty, disturbed by no false note.

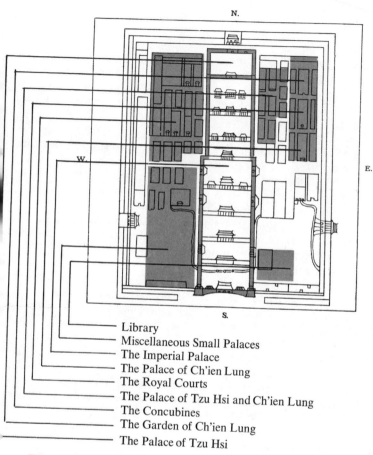

Library
Miscellaneous Small Palaces
The Imperial Palace
The Palace of Ch'ien Lung
The Royal Courts
The Palace of Tzu Hsi and Ch'ien Lung
The Concubines
The Garden of Ch'ien Lung
The Palace of Tzu Hsi

The Main Palaces of the Forbidden City

Visiting the Forbidden City

The City has been transformed into a vast museum that you can visit freely. On weekdays throughout the year and on Sundays in winter some of the lateral pavilions are open only in rotation. (Unfortunately one whole section of the palace remains permanently closed, simply because it has not yet been put in order.) On summer Sundays, however, all the rooms are open to the public, hence this is clearly a good day for your visit. A Sunday visit also affords the picturesque sight of serious and respectful crowds of Chinese who come with placid curiosity to admire the beauties offered them. You can see little old women with tiny feet, more or less being carried in the arms of great strapping youths in uniform; or groups from Tibet or Mongolia wandering around in silence, seemingly lost in the heart of the capital; whole families, strings of tiny children in tow, climb up and down the marble stairways. Today the Forbidden City belongs to everyone—but one must admit that, as a result, the palaces lose a certain majesty and some of the showcases are almost invisible because of the crowds. Sunday may be a good day for a walk in the palaces, but you can *see* them better during the week.

A final warning: the Forbidden City unfortunately has its own network of loudspeakers, which blare out a ceaseless flow of commentaries and propaganda. Count yourself lucky that you can't understand.

To see the façades of all the palaces, you should enter the City by the south. Cars can pass under the archway of the T'ien An Men gate, and after traversing a second gateway (Tuan Men) and a long avenue, they can be left in front of Wu Men (*the Meridian Gate*—1 on City plan).

The Forbidden City is made up of one central ensemble (the six imperial palaces set in line with a garden behind them) and then the wings. To the northwest are the former private apartments of the emperors and empresses. To the southwest are the former libraries, and also various palaces and temples that are rarely open. To the northeast, alongside the imperial palaces, are the former apartments of the concubines, and along the outside wall are the private palaces of Ch'ien Lung and Tzu Hsi (see Plan Number 4).

As well as the palaces and pavilions themselves, the Forbidden City contains many works of art displayed in museums. A visit to these is also interesting, but, if you have the time, you should not visit the museums at the same time as the palaces but come back and look at them at your leisure. This guide will describe the different parts of the Forbidden City before dealing with the museums. And to enable you to find your way more easily amid the maze of corridors and pavilions in the

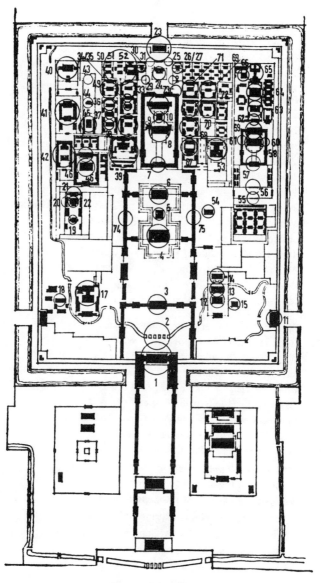

The Forbidden City

THE FACE OF PEKING

1. Wu Men—Meridian Gate
2. Golden Water River
3. T'ai Ho Men—Gate of Great Harmony
4. T'ai Ho Tien—Hall of Supreme Harmony
5. Chung Ho Tien—Hall of Complete Harmony
6. Pao Ho Tien—Hall of Preserving Harmony (Museum of Art History)
7. Ch'ien Ch'ing Men—Gate of Resplendent Purity
8. Ch'ien Ch'ing Kung—Palace of Heavenly Purity
9. Chiao T'ai Tien—Hall of Union (*or* of Imperial Marriage Rites)
10. K'un Ning Kung—Palace of Earthly Tranquillity
11. Hua Men
12. Wen Hua Tien—Palace of Literary Glory
13. Ch'u Ching Tien—Palace Where the Masters Are Honored
14. Wen Yuan Kuo—Pavilion of Depth of Knowledge
15. Ch'uan Hsin Tien—Pavilion of Intellectual Honors
16. Hsieh Ho Men—Gate of Harmonious Unity
17. Wu Ying Tien—Palace of Military Bravery
18. Hsien An Kung—Palace of Perfect Peace
19. Tsu Ming Kung—Garden of Peace and Tranquillity (*or* of the Forgotten Favorites)
20. Chi Yun Lu—Tower of Propitious Clouds
21. Hsien Jo Kuan—House of Public Weal
22. Li Hsi Ting—Pavilion of Threat of Fire
23. Shen Wu Men—Gate of Godly Prowess
24. Ch'in An Tien—Palace of Imperial Peace
25. Caves of the House of the Fairies
26. Li Tsao T'ang—Palace of Peach Trees and Reeds
27. Fu Pi T'ing—Pavilion of the Floating Jade
28. Wan Ch'un T'ing—Pavilion of the Ten Thousand Springs
29. Ping Ch'iu T'ing—Pavilion of Punctual Autumn
30. Ch'eng Jui T'ing—Pavilion of Propitious Clarity
31. Yen Hui Ko—Palace of Lasting Glory
32. Li Ching Hsuan—Gate of Beautiful Viewpoints
33. Ch'iu Hsiu Kung—Palace of Supreme Grace
34. T'i Ho Tien—Palace of Propitious Harmony
35. I K'un Kung—Palace of Help to the Emperor
36. Ch'ang Ch'un Kung—Palace of Eternal Spring
37. T'i Huan Tien—Palace of Eternal Spring

38. T'ai Chi Tien—Palace of Supreme Happiness
39. Yang Hsin Tien—Palace of Mental Cultivation
40. Ying Hua Tien—Palace of Heroic Splendor
41. Shou An Kung—Palace of Peace in Old Age
42. Shou K'ang Kung—Palace of Strength in Old Age
43. Hsi Hua Yuan—Garden of Western Flowers
44. Pao Hua Tien—Palace of Precious Splendor
45. Yu Hua Kuo—Pavilion of Rain and Water
46. T'zu Ning Kung—Palace of Peace and Tranquillity
47. Ta Fo Tang—Great Palace of Buddha
48. Yung Shou Kung—Palace of Eternal Longevity
49. Hsien Fu King—Palace of Complete Happiness
50. Chung Hua Kung—Palace of Powerful Glory
51. Chung Ching Tien—Palace of Honor
52. So Fang Chai—Pavilion of the Purest Perfumes
53. Feng Hsien Tien—Palace of Ancestral Worship
54. Museum of the Stone Drums
55. Chiu Lung Pi—Nine Dragon Wall
56. Huang Chi Men—Gate of Imperial Supremacy
57. Ning Shou Men—Gate of Peace and Longevity
58. Huang Chi Tien—Palace of Imperial Supremacy
59. Ning Shou Kung—Palace of Peace and Longevity
60 – 61. Museum of Paintings
62. Yang Hsing Men—Gate of the Cultivation of Character
63. Yang Hsing Tien—Palace of the Cultivation of Character
64. Lo Shou T'ang—Palace of Pleasure and Longevity
65. { I Ho Hsuan—Porch of the Mingling of Harmonies
{ Ching Ch'i Ko—Pavilion of the Great Happiness
66. Pi Lo Ting—Pavilion of the Jade Seashell
67. Chai Kung—Palace of Delights (Museum of Bronzes)
68. Ching Jan Kung—Palace of Prosperity (Museum of Bronzes)
69. Ch'ang Ch'ien Kung—Palace of Heavenly Favor ⎫ (Museum
                                                  ⎬ of
70. Yung Ho Kung—Palace of Eternal Harmony ⎭ Ceramics)
71. Chung Sui Kung—Palace of Purity in Affection ⎫ (Museum
                                                  ⎬ of
72. Ching Yan Kung—Palace of the Southward View ⎭ Fabrics)
73. Museum of Clocks
74 – 75. Museum of Art History
76. Chang Ye Ko—Pavilion of Melodious Sounds

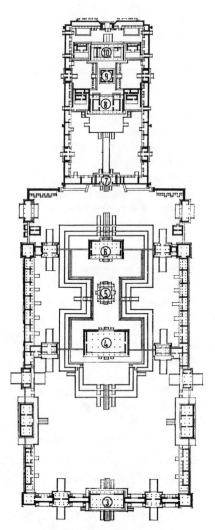

**Detail of the Central District of
The Forbidden City**

THE FORBIDDEN CITY

imperial palaces, each building has been given a number, which you can easily locate on Plan Number 5 with its key.

The Imperial Palaces

The Meridian Gate (Wu Men; 1) is a massive construction with vast wooden doors that looks more like a fortified palace than a simple gateway. From its summit the emperor used to preside over military parades, and here the new calendar was distributed each year.

Beyond the Wu Men there stretches one of the City's finest courtyards. The *Golden Water River* (2) winds its way here, crossed by five marble bridges. You should wander at your leisure all around this courtyard, for it offers superb views of the next gateway, the *Gate of Great Harmony* (T'ai Ho Men; 3), which opens onto the palaces. A long elegant construction, guarded by two bronze lions, it is in sharp contrast to the fortresslike Wu Men. The emperor used to ascend its twenty-eight steps carried in a chair over a beautiful marble flagstone decorated with dragons.

The next courtyard is the largest in the entire precinct. Here the civil servants and all the Chinese dignitaries would crowd together for official receptions; here the Allied troops marched in procession in 1918, while a Chinese general was marching down the Champs Élysées. Beyond this courtyard, which, like the previous one, is worth a long visit, rises the *Hall of Supreme Harmony* (T'ai Ho Tien; 4).

The Imperial halls and palaces are made up of two groups of three palaces each, one following the other: first the official palaces, or "front palaces," which are the more grand and imposing ones, then the private or "rear" palaces, which lie immediately behind the front ones, but to which access was strictly regulated. The T'ai Ho Tien is the first of the front palaces. It is built on a fine marble terrace similar to that of the Temple of the Heavens. Its three successive flights of steps are decorated with eighteen bronze tripods, representing the eighteen Chinese provinces. And it is worth taking a look at the symbolic turtle-dragons, cranes, corn measures, and sun-dials that decorate the terrace. The palace itself, flanked with monumental gates, is supported by three fine columns erected on a single base of hardwood. Above is a magnificent coffered roof, with a gilded dragon writhing in its middle. The emperor's

119

throne, where on major feast days he received the congratulations of the Court, is a high chair set on a platform, surrounded by chandeliers, statuettes of elephants and cranes, and complicated incense-burners.

Then come the two other official palaces. First, the *Hall of Complete Harmony* (Chung Ho Tien; 5), square, smaller, and more intimate than the T'ai Ho Tien: here the emperor got himself ready before going to the T'ai Ho Tien and here Kuang Hsu was arrested in 1898. Next, the *Hall of Preserving Harmony* (Pao Ho Tien; 6), built on the model of the T'ai Ho Tien: here the students who had passed their official examinations were received by the king. This hall contains some very fine ancient monumental bronzes (see pp. 130–131).

The private palaces lie beyond a further gate, the *Gate of Resplendent Purity* (Ch'ien Ch'ing Men; 7), which has the distinction of being the oldest monument of the Forbidden City. All the other palaces were burned down and rebuilt several times. The *Palace of Heavenly Purity* (Ch'ien Ch'ing Kung; 8), for instance, has suffered three fires since the epoch of Yung Lo. The Ming used it as a residence and the Manchu as a chamber for private audiences. In the little room on the left the emperor T'ung Chih died. The role that his mother, Tzu Hsi, played in his death has never been clearly established, but the dowager empress is said to have criticized him with extraordinary violence in front of his wife, the beautiful Aleuté, while he was dying of smallpox.

In front of the Ch'ien Ch'ing Kung two enormous banquets for a thousand and two thousand people respectively were offered by the Manchu monarchs in 1711 and 1785 for the old people of Peking. In 1785 the sons of Ch'ien Lung acted as waiters to their guests.

The next two palaces are built on the same terrace. The *Hall of Union*, or of *Imperial Marriage Rites,* (Chiao T'ai Tien; 9) is a small pavilion similar to the Hall of Complete Harmony. A modest-sized throne stands here, surrounded by twenty-five imperial seals covered with yellow cloths; the curious hydraulic clock to the right was made for Ch'ien Lung. The *Palace of Earthly Tranquillity* (K'un Ning Kung; 10) was the residence of the Ming empresses. In the western part of this palace the Manchu emperors carried out curious secret shaman

THE FORBIDDEN CITY

rites, a kind of sacred pantomime dating back thousands of years, in which hunting themes were performed at birthday parties and initiation ceremonies. A part of the building was dedicated solely to the god of cuisine. Later this wing served as a bridal chamber.

To leave the central precinct, you must go back through the Gate of Resplendent Purity.

The former libraries

This group of palaces, southwest of the Forbidden City, are open today only for temporary exhibitions. But you can easily see them from the outside, for they are in the part of the Forbidden City that you cross if you enter it by Hua Men (11).

The Golden Water River curves around a high-walled enclosure. The first of the palaces in this enclosure is the *Palace of Literary Glory* (Wen Hua Tien; 12), where the "Festival of the Classics" was celebrated in olden days, during the second month of the lunar calendar. It was one of that era's supreme centers of the intellectual life.

Behind the Wen Hua Tien is the Ch'u Ching Tien, the *Palace Where the Masters Are Honored* (13), dedicated to Confucius and his teachings. Here lectures were given for members of the Court and the emperor discussed personally the texts of Confucius, in an atmosphere less ceremonial than that of the Hall of the Classics (see chapter on the temples of Peking, pp 149–168). The gilded roofs of the Wen Hua Tien and the Ch'u Ching Tien are among the finest of the Forbidden City, perfect examples of orthodox Chinese architecture. The admirable decorations of the gables are worth noting. At the far end of the enclosure lies the blue-tiled three-story *Pavilion of Depth of Knowledge* (Wen Yuan Ko; 14), an imperial library founded by Ch'ien Lung that used to house classical, philosophical, historical, and literary texts.

To the east of the Wen Hua Tien is the *Palace of Intellectual Honors* (Ch'uan Hsin Tien; 15), where sacrificial rites were held in honor of philosophers and leading artists.

From here you return to the courtyard of the Golden Water River by the *Gate of Harmonious Unity* (Hsieh Ho Men; 16), used at the beginning of the eighteenth century by K'ang Hsi to leave the palace incognito.

THE FACE OF PEKING

The small palaces

While you can at least look around the outside of the former libraries in the southeast corner, the whole of the southwest section of the Imperial City is today completely closed to the public; through forgotten gateways left slightly ajar you can glimpse soldiers playing basketball. . . . Perhaps one day those soldiers will find other playing fields and leave this part of the City to the public again. Meanwhile, we shall give only the briefest details of its palaces.

In the section that corresponds in the east to the libraries in the west, there are two interesting buildings. The *Palace of Military Bravery* (Wu Ying Tien; 17) used to be the imperial printing house where the writings of the emperors were printed, in particular the poems of Ch'ien Lung; after 1911 collections of porcelain and bronze were exhibited here. Farther west is the *Palace of Perfect Peace* (Hsin An Kung; 18), a school where "western" languages were taught—Mongol, Tibetan, Turkestan.

Farther north lies the *Garden of Peace and Tranquillity,* otherwise known as the *Garden of the Forgotten Favorites* (Tsu Ning Kung; 19), which contains various Tibetan temples including a *Tower of Propitious Clouds* (Chi Yun Lou; 20), decorated with ceramics from Tibet representing ten thousand Buddhas. The other main buildings in this garden are the *House of Public Weal* (Hsien Jo Kuan; 21) and the *Pavilion of Threat of Fire* (Li Hsi T'ing; 22).

You enter the *Garden of Ch'ien Lung* in the north part of the City, directly if you approach the Forbidden City through the *Gate of Military Genius* (Shen Wu Men; 23), the northern gate facing the Hill of Coal. The garden is a marvelous ensemble of century-old trees (the finest cypresses in Peking), flowers, bushes, artificial grottoes, and pools overhung by rocks. Ch'ien Lung loved to stroll here, surrounded by a few favorites, and here he composed some of his admired poems. An extraordinary calm still pervades this garden and at the height of summer it is a haven of freshness.

In the center of the garden is the *Palace of Imperial Peace* (Ch'in An Tien; 24), a temple dedicated to the god of fire, surrounded by a precinct guarded by two bronze monsters. In front of the gate are two interlacing trees. The palace, set on a marble terrace, is covered with a fine projecting roof and then a double rooftop crowned with a small stupa made of huge gilded ridge tiles.

To the east of the garden you can see the *Caves of the House of the Fairies* (25), decorated with two lovely stone fountains; Ch'ien Lung's private library (the *Palace of Peach Trees and Reeds*) (26); the *Pavilion of the Floating Jade* (Fu Pi T'ing; 27), built over a pool and unfortunately recently repainted; and the fine *Pavilion of the Ten Thousand Springs* (Wan Ch'ung T'ing; 28) on a marble terrace.

In the west part of the garden are the *Pavilion of Punctual Autumn* (Ping Ch'iu T'ing; 29), a replica of the *Pavilion of Ten Thousand Springs*; a temple dedicated to the god of literature, the *Pavilion of Propitious Clarity* (Ch'eng Jui T'ing; 30), built over a small lake; and a suite of waiting rooms where the emperor's visitors rested and took refreshments. Known as the *Palace of Lasting Glory* (Yen Hui Ko; 31), it has a remarkably tortured roof, intended to be purely decorative, and is still furnished.

The private residences

The entire northwest part of the Forbidden City is a succession of courtyards, palaces, and pavilions, its apparent disorder contrasting with the disciplined arrangement of the City's other buildings. In these palaces the kings and their wives actually lived, in a setting rather more suited to everyday life than that of the palaces, however "private," of the central enclosure.

Many of these pavilions are not open to the public because they have not yet been completely rearranged or cleared of ancillary services. First the pavilions you *can* visit are described; then, very summarily, the others in this part of the City.

Pavilions open to visitors

Only three groups of pavilions are open:

Leading palaces of Tzu Hsi and of the last empress. These are four pavilions in a row, surrounded by fine tranquil courtyards and watched over by superb bronze animals—tortoises, cranes, pheasants, hinds, and stags. These little palaces are furnished in late-nineteenth-century imperial style in which traditional Chinese is married to Western influence. From north to south they are:

The Gate of Beautiful Viewpoints (Li Ching Hsuan; 32), sometimes closed to the public.

The Palace of Supreme Grace (Ch'u Hsiu Kung; 33), where Wan Jung lived, the beautiful wife of the last emperor Hsuan T'ung. In its center is a throne room and to the east a bedroom decorated with embroideries and with curious clocks made by European artisans. To the west is a reception room with a most extraordinary clock in gilded bronze, set on the statue of a camel and decorated with birds.

The Palace of Propitious Harmony (Ti Ho Tien; 34) is decorated with fine glass paintings and cloisonné tables full of trinkets.

The Palace of Help to the Emperor (I K'un Kung; 35) was inhabited by various empresses, including Tzu Hsi after her arrival at the Court. The interior is made up of several bedrooms where each object on view is at once intriguing and in exquisitely bad taste. Note especially the huge brass fruits and the elephants in silver cloisonné.

Little palaces of concubines and second residence of Tzu Hsi. Some favorite concubines used to live in the emperors' private apartments, among them Li Fei, the leading concubine of the Ming emperor T'ien Ch'i. The group of pavilions where they lived is immediately to the west of the group described above. It includes, from north to south:

The Palace of Eternal Spring (Ch'ang Ch'ien Kung; 36) is surrounded by an elegant veranda and fronted by a fine court-yard whose walls are painted in charmingly *trompe-l'oeil* scenes taken from the earliest realistic Chinese novel, *The Dream of the Red Chamber*. The palace itself, which was inhabited by Li Fei and by Tzu Hsi during the reign of her son T'ung Chih contains fine tapestries, paintings, and coffers full of jewels.

The Palace of the Basis of Property (Ti Huan Tien; 37) is divided into several rooms by heavy partitions made of carved black wood. It contains some huge blue cloisonnés, and note also the low bed (*k'ang*) that was heated in winter by a fire lighted underneath it. Several concubines lived in this palace.

The Palace of Supreme Happiness (T'ai Chi Tien; 38) was also inhabited by several empresses. Tzu Hsi decorated it herself with calligraphic scrolls, and one exhibit is an extraordinary mechanical ventilator in cloisonné.

The Palace of Mental Cultivation. This huge enclosure lies to the south of the two preceding ones. T'ung Chih, Kuang Hsu, and Hsuan T'ung, the three hapless Manchu monarchs, lived there. Here Kuang Hsu died, a few hours before Tzu Hsi herself, refusing to clothe himself in the yellow imperial garments on the grounds that he was not worthy of them. Until 1924 the Republic set aside this part of the palace for Hsuan T'ung (who later became Pu Yi; see page 25).

The Palace of Mental Cultivation (39), made up of a central unit and dependencies, is fronted by a fine pai-lou and guarded by gilded-bronze lions. The interior is finely preserved: in the middle a throne room, all in gold, yellow, and blue, contains a fine library; to the east is a handsome room with light-colored woodwork, its floor covered with a large gold carpet; to the west is a study; and in front a small studio where the emperors wrote and sketched (note the writing set of pale jade).

Pavilions at present closed

The most important of the pavilions closed to the public are:

The Palace of Heroic Splendor (Ying Hua Tien; 40), in the north corner of the City, which formerly had a fine garden in front of it.

The Palace of Peace in Old Age (Shou An Kung; 41), south of the above.

The Palace of Strength in Old Age (Shou K'ang Kung; 42), once inhabited by several concubines.

The Garden of Western Flowers (Hsi Hua Yuan; 43), to the east of the Ying Hua Tien. A pavilion holding a part of the Manchu treasure was mysteriously burned to the ground in 1923, and the treasure vanished in smoke and ashes. Rumor has it that certain people found this explanation of its disappearance rather convenient. . . .

The Palace of Precious Splendor (Pao Hua Tien; 44), originally a Taoist temple under the Ming, later an important Buddhist temple often visited by the emperors.

The Pavilion of Rain and Water (Yu Hua Kuo; 45), the beautiful four-story building dominating this entire part of the City, is one of the most curious. Note from the outside the strange dragons rampant on its roof. It is a Lamaist temple where once there were fearsome Tibetan idols decorated with human bones and erotic statues (are they still there today?).

The Palace of Peace and Tranquillity (T'zu Ning Kung; 46) is the most important building in this part of the City. It was lived in by the dowager empress mother of Ch'ien Lung, and later by Tzu An, the "empress of the west" (she lived in the west part of the City), coregent with Tzu Hsi (who lived in the east). Tzu An died in 1881, probably poisoned by Tzu Hsi.

The Great Palace of Buddha (Ta Fo Tang; 47), another important Buddhist temple, adorned with numerous statues.

The Palace of Eternal Longevity (Yung Shou Kung; 48) was the home of various concubines.

The Palace of Complete Happiness (Hsien Fu Kung; 49) was used by Tzu Hsi as an exhibition hall for her treasures.

Finally, the three small palaces in the corner of this part of the City were lived in by Ch'ien Lung during his youth, and included a theater (50, 51, 52).

The palaces of Ch'ien Lung and Tzu Hsi

Set in the northeast corner of the Forbidden City, these can easily be reached from the long courtyard that separates the two central groups of palaces. A gate opens onto a huge empty space that you cross diagonally.

To the left is the high-walled precinct of the *Palace of Ancestral Worship* (Feng Hsien Tien; 53), which is open only for special exhibitions. To the right a small isolated pavilion contains the *Museum of the Stone Drums* (54). In the western wall of this courtyard a fine ceramic gate opens onto the group of palaces built by Ch'ien Lung from 1773–77. This great Manchu emperor, after reigning for sixty years, decided that he would be lacking in respect to his ancestor K'ang Hsi if he remained on the throne longer than the latter had. So he abdicated, handing over power to his son Chia Ch'ing and quitting the imperial palaces to go and live in the east part of the City. He lived there for four years, and Tzu Hsi came to live there in her turn after 1889.

These palaces are in fact divided into two groups: the enclosure of buildings known as the *Palaces of Peace and Longevity*, admirably sober in style and a kind of refined copy of the central imperial palaces; next, a rather more confused succession of pavilions and rooms, set farther to the north and greatly rebuilt by Tzu Hsi.

THE FORBIDDEN CITY

The Palaces of Peace and Longevity. These are one of the finest groups of palaces in all the Forbidden City. Though modest in size, they reach a kind of perfection in the simplicity of their lines and the delicacy of their decoration. You should visit them early in the morning when they are empty: sit on a balustrade beside a terrace, and you will share something of the mystery of this eternal city.

The gates and palaces run from south to north:

The Nine Dragon Wall (Chiu Lung Pi; 55), with its multi-colored baroque monsters, is regarded as even more perfect than that of Pei Hai.

The Gate of Imperial Supremacy (Huang Chi Men; 56) forms a triumphal pai-lou in front of the emperors' palaces and opens onto a first courtyard that is quiet and shady.

The Gate of Peace and Longevity (Ning Shou Kung; 57) leads to the palaces.

The Palace of Imperial Supremacy (Huang Chi Tien; 58) is set on a beautiful terrace with marble balustrades. To left and right are fine decorative motifs in white marble. The palace itself was a small room for receiving visitors, later used by Tzu Hsi until 1900.

The Palace of Peace and Longevity (Ning Chou Tien; 59) was the very heart of the residence of Ch'ien Lung, where secret shaman rites were performed for the aging emperor. In her turn Tzu Hsi took it over in 1900.

Two museums of paintings have been established in the side pavilions (60, 61) of this enclosure.

The last palaces of Ch'ien Lung and Tzu Hsi. Beyond the Palaces of Peace and Longevity, you enter a new enclosure by the *Gate of the Cultivation of Character* (Yang Hsing Men; 62). The group of palaces inside this enclosure today forms the museum of jewels and precious objects of the Manchu dynasty, and you must pay 5 fen to get in.

The first courtyard is pleasantly shady and opens at the right onto the beautiful private theater of Tzu Hsi: the three-story *Pavilion of Melodious Sounds*, where important stage sets were kept. On the north side of the courtyard is the *Palace of the Cultivation of Character* (Yang Hsing Tien; 63), a typically Manchu construction, much more ornate and encumbered than the preceding palaces. Beyond another charming courtyard, decorated with a few bronzes and a wall, you arrive at the huge *Palace of Pleasure and Longevity* (Lo Shan T'ang; 64), which housed Ch'ien Lung's library and, on the west side, Tzu Hsi's sitting room. The walls of the galleries are covered with steles inscribed with Ch'ien Lung's poems. The final palace (65) is made up of the *Porch of the Mingling of Harmonies* (I Ho Hsuan) and the *Pavilion of the Great Happiness* (Ching Ch'i Ko), linked by a covered gallery that opens onto little gardens. You walk through this gallery on the western side in front of the *Pavilion of the Jade Seashell* (Pi Lo Ting; 66), perched high on artificial rocks amid pretty bushes. Ch'ien Lung wrote poetry here—he seems to have written it almost everywhere!

A few yards from the exit of this enclosure you can see on your right, if you look carefully, a well covered with a heavy stone lid. Into this well the concubine of Kuang Hsu, the beautiful Chen Fei, was thrown for remarking to Tzu Hsi, as the latter was quitting her palace after the defeat of the Boxers, that running away wasn't a very civilized way to behave.

The Museums of the Forbidden City

The imperial palaces as a whole are just one big museum. Among them the pavilions specially arranged as museum halls house some admirable artistic collections.

Halls of history and Chinese art. This group is made up of the Pao Ho Tien (6) and the two side galleries (74 and 75) that run along the front palaces. It is best to visit them in this order—Pao Ho Tien, east gallery (74), west gallery (75)— and together they provide a summary of Chinese art from its origins until today.

The *Pao Ho Tien* includes a fine collection of bronzes, ceramics, and semiprecious stones, from the legendary epoch (4000–2000 B.C.) to the beginning of the Warring States period (480 B.C.).

You visit the hall from left to right. The first showcases (1–5) include some fine ancient ceramics (whose shapes resemble certain Greek and Cretan vases) and carved semiprecious stones. Next come huge Shang bronzes—especially a fine tripod (case 9)—and an array of clocks and horse harnesses (case 13). All the cases from 9 to 19 are devoted to the Shang dynasty, whose bronzes are the finest of all, superb in their simplicity. Next, in cases 20–27 are the bronzes of the first Chou epoch, and in cases 28–32 the monumental bronzes of the second Chou period (780–480 B.C.).

The most northerly hall is devoted to bronzes and articles of daily use of the Warring States. Hall 2 testifies to the emergence of engravings on stone (Ch'in period, 221–206 B.C.; Han period, 206 B.C.–A.D. 220). Themes of horses and hunting, soon to become very common, make their first appearance. There are also huge stone rams, dating from the first Han kings, that seem to have emerged from the days of prehistory. Hall 3, entirely devoted to Han bronzes and ceramics, contains in particular some huge finely chiseled bronze drums. Hall 4 covers the years 221–580 that is, the period of the Three Kingdoms and the rival dynasties of the north and south. Printing now appears, and scrolls of painted silk, and it is worth noting a fine Buddha in white stone, and funeral statuettes.

In Hall 5 are exhibited the artistic splendor of the Sui and T'ang periods (580–907): two fine T'ang murals, superbly ironic; draped statues of Greek inspiration; and, in Hall 6, an array of ceramic funeral statuettes and huge horses. In this same hall are some fine blue and black pieces of pottery (a drum, among others) and the first "three colors" ceramics. Hall 7 marks the beginning of the Five Dynasties (907–960), the Liao (961–1125), their contemporaries further south, the Sung (960–1279), and the Kin (1115 –1234): there are some fine Sung paintings on yellow backgrounds and two great gilded Buddhas. In Hall 8 there are beautiful white and green jades and *blancs de Chine*.

The *West Gallery* (74) covers the "modern" period of Chinese art: from the Mongol (Yuan) to the Manchu (Ch'ing). Hall 1, the most southerly, is entirely devoted to a huge magnificent Yuan Buddhist fresco from Shansi Province. In Hall 2 the only exhibits are photographs of Yuan paintings whose originals are now in Taiwan. Hall 3 includes artistic objects of this same dynasty—figures of Buddhas, blue-and-white porcelain. Hall 4 opens the way to the Ming dynasty: paintings of fine landscapes and flowers, embroidered birds. In Hall 5 there are ceramics, cloisonnés, lacquered and woven articles, all of them Ming—the cloisonnés are especially worth noting. From Hall 6 onward the rooms are devoted to the last

Manchu dynasty. First, paintings—lovely painted tea flowers—and embroidered silks. Hall 7 is devoted to ceramics and to woven and lacquered works of the Ch'ing period (including a fine ten-panel K'ang Hsi screen). In Hall 8 are jewels, clothing, and statuettes of the eighteenth century, and in Hall 9 paintings from the end of the Manchu period.

Museums of Paintings (60 and 61): The two lateral wings of Ch'ien Lung's imperial palaces house exhibitions of paintings. Because of the quality and abundance of Chinese painting —and whatever the so-called experts may say, all the best Chinese paintings are *not* in Taipeh—these two wings are generally devoted to temporary exhibitions that are changed frequently. Details therefore cannot be given here, but the exhibits are usually of high interest. The two galleries open alternately. The only snag is that there are no written details of any sort in any Western language—not even dates—to give the average inexpert visitor some notion of what he is admiring.

The museums of bronzes, ceramics, and fabrics. The former palaces of the concubines are entirely devoted to bronzes, ceramics, and embroideries. They are all built roughly on the same model: in the middle of a square precinct bordered with outbuildings, two elegant pavilions stand on stone terraces. These little courtyards are set in pairs, and a few trees and a well help to give a pleasant atmosphere.

The bronzes: Two adjacent precincts (67 and 68) are open on Mondays, Fridays, and Sundays. The bronzes on show, the finest in Peking, are grouped not by epoch but by type of object (ritual vases, amphoras, etc.). No object is later than the period of the Warring States. Information about most of the objects is given in Chinese characters, but occasionally "modern Chinese" transcription is used—the system employed in the details given below.

In the precinct of the *Palace of Delights* (Chai Kung; 67) there are two adjacent pavilions. *First pavilion*: in the center and on the left are *ding*, or ritual vases of the Shang, Chou, or Warring States periods, tripodic or square; on the right are *li* and *yan*, utensils for daily use. *Second pavilion*: in the left hall and the left part of the central hall are *gui*, cooking utensils, originally in bamboo and later in bronze, of the Shang, Cho, and

Warring States periods; in· the right-hand part of the central hall are *dou*, which were used for holding meat and vegetables and whose shapes were copied for oil lamps in the eighth to fifth centuries B.C.; in the right-hand hall are kitchen instruments of the Western Chou and Warring States periods.

The precinct of the *Palace of Prosperity* (Ching Jen Kung; 68) is where Chen Fei ("the Pearl Concubine") lived in the 1890s, and contains little else but amphoras for wine. At the rear of the left-hand hall are *zun*, jars for holding alcohol dating from the early Shang period. In the left-hand part of the left hall and the left part of the central hall are *jia*, flat- or round-bottomed vases of the Shang epoch. In the north part of the central hall are *pei*, domestic utensils of the Shang period, as well as two-handled or four-handled *ling* vases from the ninth and seventh centuries B.C., and *yu* vases of the Shang and Western Chou periods. In the right of the central hall and in the right-hand hall are *hu*, wine jars of the Chou and Warring States periods. Note the fine vase from the latter period, decorated with dragons, in the center of the right-hand hall.

The ceramics: Two precincts side by side, open on Tuesdays, Fridays, and Sundays (69 and 70).

The precinct of the *Palace of Celestial Favour* (Ch'eng Ch'ien Kung; 69) is made up of two pavilions. The *first pavilion* houses objects ranging from earthenware of the fourth millennium B.C. to the Yuan (Mongol) ceramics. Note the fine Sung works in cases 14–21 (celadons, *blancs de Chine*, etc.). The Yuan porcelain is exhibited in the right hall of the pavilion. The *second pavilion* has all the Ming ceramics, one of the finest art collections in the Forbidden City. There is a fine variety of "blue-and-whites."

The precinct of the *Palace of Eternal Harmony* (Yung Ho Kung; 70) is also made up of two pavilions. The *first pavilion* has Ch'ing polychrome porcelain, laid out not chronologically but according to type of decoration. It is easy to note in each case the decadence of the art of porcelain after the days of Ch'ien Lung. The *second pavilion* has monochrome Ch'ing porcelain: celadons, yellows, *sangs-de-boeuf*, "snowy" blue-greens, etc.

Fabrics: two precincts side by side (71 and 72) are open on Wednesdays, Saturdays, and Sundays. They are not of much interest save to specialists—except for the fine carpets in precinct 72.

The precinct of the *Palace of Purity in Affection* (Chang Sui Kung; 71) has two pavilions. In the *first pavilion* are fabrics earlier than the Ming period (the oldest date back to the Sung) but only small woven fragments have survived. The *second pavilion* has Ming embroideries and woven cloths.

The precinct of the *Palace of the Southward View* (Ching Yan Kung; 72): in the first courtyard some outbuildings contain fine Ch'ing carpets—yellow, blue, gilded, etc.; then two adjacent pavilions house Ch'ing embroideries and woven fabrics, court robes, decorative panels, and screens.

The Museum of Stone Drums. This (54) is in the small isolated pavilion between the principal palaces and those of Ch'ien Lung. Its ten stone drums are the oldest relics of Chinese sculpture: they go back to the seventh century B.C. (Chou dynasty) and were discovered fifteen hundred years later in Shansi Province. In the thirteenth century A.D. they were placed in the temple of Confucius. Strictly speaking, they are not drums but blocks of sculpted stone in the shape of drums on which are carved precious inscriptions: ten ancient odes in irregular verse. The same pavilion also contains inscriptions on stone dating from the epoch of the Warring States.

The Museum of Clocks. Located in the northeast part of the precinct of the rear palaces, this museum (73) is open from 10 a.m. and can be visited, only in groups, every forty-five minutes. It includes a number of eighteenth-century English, French and Chinese performing clocks: birds beat their wings, ducks scud along, musicians play the violin, fountains play in a highly finished setting of silver and gilded bronze.

The Treasures of the Ch'ing Dynasty. The further palace of Ch'ien Lung (63, 64, 65) contains the treasures of the Manchu dynasty, an extraordinary accumulation of gold, semiprecious stones, and other objects often intricate and worthless. The *first pavilion* (63) holds jade musical instruments and golden clocks; on the west side there are golden cups. The *second pavilion* (64) has jewels in its central hall, and in its side hall some incredible model pagodas and stupas in solid gold. Note also a huge carved semiprecious stone. The *third pavilion* (65) is devoted to jade.

MODERN PEKING

"Modern Peking" is grafted onto the old city like some unsightly excrescence. You see on arrival: the airport, the station, a huge wide avenue, T'ien An Men Square. Perhaps you can forget this modern city when you wander in the alleys of the old town—but that will not please your guides, who themselves are very proud of the huge new buildings dating mostly from 1958. The English-language *Guide to Peking* published by the Chinese authorities offers a wealth of information about this new Peking, and below are a few details.

T'ien An Men Square (general map, E5). T'ien An Men ("the Gate of Heavenly Peace") "is not only a building of some artistic and historical value, but also a place of political significance. The gate, with its imposing tower, is the very essence of the national emblem of the new China"—so runs the official Chinese guidebook in English. This gate forms the north side of a gigantic square where all the big ceremonies of the regime take place. In the center of the square, on a two-tiered marble terrace, is the monument to the Heroes of the Revolution. Mao Tse-tung laid its corner stone in 1949, but it was officially opened only in 1958. The statue is rather more austere than most Western war memorials.

THE FACE OF PEKING

To the left and right of the square are two buildings in Mussolino-neo-Stalinian style, the *Great Hall of the People* and the *Museums of the Revolution and of Chinese History*. They are on a vast scale, and the first contains several big halls where plays or other shows are sometimes presented.

The Museum of the Revolution (general map, E5, temporarily closed). Quite apart from any political considerations, this museum is worth a visit, for it is a very model of dialectic propaganda. It is well set out, and there are really two methods of visiting it: in half an hour or in four hours. That is, alone and fast or with a Chinese guide who will explain to you the semimystical significance of every red flag. The exhibition as a whole illustrates different phases of the "liberation" of China, from the Opium War up to October 1, 1949. The first halls are quite bizarre: huge socialist-realist paintings show the Boxers massacring every sort of foreign imperialist, while the metal plaque that used to stand above the entrance to the International Concession in Shanghai has been symbolically inverted with its face to a wall.

After a few minor leaders of the world of revolution comes Chairman Mao himself to whom the entire museum is in fact dedicated. Hundreds of photographs, paintings, and historical tableaux show him standing, sitting, meditating, or in action. Huge maps show the route of the Long March, and in the halls at the back are trophies of the 1945–49 war against the Kuomintang.

The Military Museum of the Revolution (temporarily closed). This is in Fu Hsing Men Ta Chieh, in the western extension of Ch'ang An (general map, A5). It covers the same ground as the Museum of the Revolution but is more technical: the different military campaigns are shown with maps and diagrams. As this museum is mainly for specialists, you must apply to the China Travel Service to visit it.

The Peking Planetarium. This faces the zoo, on Hsi Chih Men Ta Chieh (general map, A2). It is similar to small planetaria around the world and is not really worth a visit unless you have nothing better to do.

MODERN PEKING

The Palace of National Minorities (general map, C5; temporarily closed). Although considered one of the splendors of modern Chinese architecture, it seems rather heavy and ill-proportioned and its attempt to marry a traditional style to modern experiment has resulted in a mongrel construction. The inside is gilded to the very limit; the outside resembles the central station or the airport, but with roofs of glazed green tiles, and the two-hundred-foot tower makes it the tallest building in Peking. Its function is to display the cultural riches of the "national minorities" who live on Chinese territory and are continually having honors paid to them.

The Center of Agricultural Exhibitions. This is outside the town on the road to the airport, and in style and inspiration it recalls the Palace of Minorities. But as it is larger and, pleasantly situated within a park, it has rather more appeal. A fine statue of a group of peasants, in the purest socialist-realist style, stands in the main courtyard.

The Exhibition Palace (general map, A2). "The Peking Exhibition Center," says the official guidebook, "was first known as the Center of the Soviet Exhibition in Peking, and is the symbol of the great friendship between the Chinese and Soviet people." The word "Soviet" has been dropped, and the place is just called the Exhibition Center. It is built in Soviet style, extremely ornate, with cupolas and a lot of gilt. The murals of the central pavilion are devoted to themes of Man and Work, in a monumental style. The doors are highly gilded. And the place is worth visiting only if you have business there.

THE HISTORICAL MUSEUM

This is a palace opposite the Palace of Congress, in T'ien An Men Square, its entrance on the southern side of the building, facing the monument to the Heroes of the Revolution. The museum, closed during the Cultural Revolution, is expected to reopen soon.

Apart from the museums of the Forbidden City (and, in a different way, that of the Revolution), this is the only museum in Peking of real interest to a Westerner. It was installed in its present huge building on T'ien An Men Square in 1959; before that, inside the Forbidden City itself was a museum of Peking history probably much less well arranged than this new *Chinese Historical Museum*, which offers a complete panorama—well laid out, though sometimes a bit too didactic—of the different periods of Chinese art and it offers an ideal introduction to Chinese history and art history. The history is, of course, ideologically slanted—the story of the first appearance of bronze or porcelain is told with much detail of serfs revolting against brutal masters—but you can always ignore the proselytism and concentrate on the porcelain.

The museum has two floors, each containing four galleries set in a rectangle around a courtyard.

The *ground floor* covers the historical period from the earliest days of Chinese art to the rival dynasties of north and south (A.D. 589). Beyond an anteroom displaying two fine copies from the Sung period of Han astronomical instruments, you go into the *northern gallery*, which is devoted to prehistory: a wax model of "Peking Man" (Teilhard de Chardin's famous ape-man), as well as interesting models of cave-dwellings and some early earthenware.

The first part of the *east gallery* is also devoted to prehistory: fine pottery in the form of elegant cups, and vases that might almost be Greek. Then you pass into the "legendary period" of Chinese history, with a few relics of the art of the *Hsia* (up to the seventeenth century B.C.), and then into history itself with the *Shang* (seventeenth–twelfth centuries B.C.). The first bronzes in the second part of this gallery are very fine—a huge incense-burner and a vase known as "the vase of the four sheep"—and there is also some beautiful black pottery.

The southwest corner of this gallery marks the beginning of the *Chou* period (twelfth–fifth centuries B.C.), which was the great age of bronzes—witness the huge plate, superbly worked, that was used for receiving the blood of executed criminals. There are other fine examples of the art of bronze in the first part of the *south gallery*, devoted mainly to the Chou and to the *Warring States* (476–221 B.C.) with their splendid array of lacquered objects. In the middle of the gallery are the first *Han* objects: bronzes, iron lanterns, and, at the end of the central section, the first pieces of porcelain, still rather similar to pottery. There is also a curious horse from Szechwan drawing a chariot, some lovely bronze mirrors, and, in the southwest corner, a number of funeral statuettes depicting village scenes.

In the *west gallery* are some fine copies of Han astronomical instruments, and works of art from the *Chin* dynasty (A.D. 265–420). The contrast between these and Han art is striking: gentler and more elegant, the forms prepare the way for the later miracle of the T'ang period. There are earthenware horses and camels, as well as murals, the model of an entry to a tomb, and photographs of the Yung Kang caves. Note also two present-day models of army tanks, one actually a compass and barometer, the other a drum.

THE FACE OF PEKING

On the *first floor* you make the tour of the building in the opposite direction. The *southwest gallery* is devoted to the *Sui* (581–618) and especially the *T'ang* periods, and you will find their works also in the south gallery. First there are genuine Sui glazed-porcelain objects, funeral figurines, and finally T'ang porcelain in three colors. The center of the gallery contains fine monumental horses, lines of musicians and funeral mourners, and kneeling camels. At the far end is the model of a carved and painted Kansu cave-dwelling. In the southwest corner are some T'ang murals in remarkably bold colors and a quaintly old-fashioned humor (at least by Western standards).

The beginning of the *south gallery* has more T'ang objects, then figurines dating back to the *Five Dynasties* (960–1279), then bronzes and porcelain pieces of the Sung period. By this time porcelain is true art: T'ing whites, celadons, translucent bluish whites, and the first painted decorations. In the middle of the gallery are the marvelous Sung paintings.

The *Yuan* period (1271–1368) is represented only by a few blue-and-white porcelain and red-enameled vases and by a strange hydraulic clock. The *Ming* works (1368–1644) take up the end part of this gallery and the southeast corner: all types of porcelain are on show, blue-and-white, sapphire, red, *sang-de-boeuf*, and *familles vertes*, *roses*, and *jaunes*.

The last part of the museum (east and north galleries) is devoted solely to *Manchu* art and handicrafts: paintings, lacquered objects, furniture, embroideries, woven goods. All the decadent wealth of this civilization is illustrated in the cloisonnés and the fine incense-burners in precious stone on show in the north gallery.

The visit closes with a huge poster of one of Chairman Mao's "Thoughts."

RAMPARTS, GATES, AND PARKS

As has been said, little remains today of the old ramparts and gates of Peking. The Ch'ien Men gate, on the south side of T'ien An Men Square, is the only surviving relic. During the past few years, in order to improve the movement of traffic around the capital, the Peking city council has been systematically pulling down the old walls and gates, some of which had become terrible bottlenecks. It is sad to see such fine gates disappear, such massive walls five hundred years old—but have we not done the same in the past to many Western cities, including Paris and London?

Twenty-five miles of ramparts as high as a four-story house used to surround the Tartar and Chinese Cities. The walls, originally made simply of beaten earth, in time were covered with tiles and masonry. Specialists in Chinese art and Peking history have discovered a mass of interesting material there (marked tiles, sculptures, inscriptions, and so on). Until the fall of the empire people were forbidden to walk along the path that circuited the summit of the ramparts, in case they might peer down over the red walls of the Forbidden City.

Here and there rose monumental gates, forming little crescent-shaped enclosures outside the walls themselves. And on

139

top of each inner gate (in the ramparts) and each outer gate (in the crescent-shaped enclosure) there stood a pavilion. There was thus a kind of courtyard within each pair of gates, and inside it were one or two temples, little shops, and sentry posts. Look at Ch'ien Men gate and you will get an idea of how immensely impressive this circle of ramparts was when it was still largely intact only a few years ago.

Ch'ien Men ("the Front Gate"; (general map, E6) is the most famous gate in Peking. It is set at the southern end of the triumphal avenue that starts from the imperial palaces and crosses T'ien An Men Square. And it is this gate that stands at the crossroads of this great square and forms a backdrop to all the public parades. The external gate of the Ch'ien Men was always closed, reserved in former times for the emperor alone—ordinary mortals used the little side gates in the crescent-shaped enclosure. It was through the Ch'ien Men that the emperor passed amid great pomp on his way to the Temple of Heaven. And every evening there was an elaborate ceremony for the closing of Ch'ien Men: gongs were sounded at regular intervals, then the sentries raucously warned late lingerers that they had no more than five minutes to get back into the Tartar City. Finally the heavy doors of the gate were closed, and anyone who arrived too late simply had to stay there until midnight, when Ch'ien Men, alone of all the gates in the city, was once more opened to admit into the Imperial City the civil servants of the court who had dallied amid the pleasures of the Chinese town. Anyone who has been at a boarding school or college in a Western country might find all this a little familiar.

The two pavilions of Ch'ien Men are still standing, rebuilt after the fires of 1900. The high dark bulk of each pavilion, with its elegant tiers of protruding roofs, towers up through a network of electric cables and trolley lines. The crescent-shaped enclosure has disappeared, but the two little temples that helped to protect the City against evil spirits are still there, though empty. On the east is the *Kuan Ti Temple*, dedicated to the god of war, and on the west the *Kuan Yin Temple*, dedicated to the goddess of mercy.

Ho Ping Men (general map, D6), the newest gate of the Tartar City, was built by the Kuomintang and led out toward Liu Li Chang. It has now been pulled down.

RAMPARTS, GATES, AND PARKS

Shun Chih Men ("the Gate of Direct Rule"; general map, C6) is better known under the name of *Ssu Men,* "the Gate of Death." It opened out toward the famous "Vegetable Market" (general map, C7) in the Chinese City, where condemned prisoners were executed. Up to the time of the Kuomintang you could see whole truckloads of hapless prisoners passing under the Shun Chih Men, piled one against the other, haggard-faced, escorted by shabbily dressed soldiers who clearly cared nothing for their charges' fate. Shun Chih Men had the reputation of bringing unhappiness, and no king or queen ever drove through it.

The Jesuit Observatory (general map, G5) has been preserved. Kubla Khan was the first to build a terrace more or less on this spot, from which the movement of the stars could be observed. Yung Lo largely rebuilt it, and it was again destroyed and rebuilt in the sixteenth century. The square tower that you see today is a relatively modern block of masonry built on the original foundations. It is at the far end of the one bit of rampart still standing, immediately south of Ch'ang An. There is some talk of reopening the observatory to visitors, but at present only from a distance can you admire the wrought-bronze objects on its roof which are said to be remarkable. They are instruments for measuring the skies, the work of the Jesuits, Father Adam Schall and Father Verbiest, who brought European sciences to China in the sixteenth century. Among the instruments are three spheres, a quadrant, a sextant, a celestial globe, a theodolite, and a compass given to Ch'ien Lung by Louis XIV.

The Imperial Lakes and Parks

To the west of the Forbidden City stretch vast open spaces, formerly the site of the imperial lakes and parks, and easily visible from the Hill of Coal. In early days they were marshes, but Kubla Khan had them drained when he chose this site for the palaces of the Mongol dynasty (evoked by Coleridge in his dream-poem that begins "In Xanadu did Kubla. . . ."). Out of the lakes and forests he made immense wooded parks (described by Marco Polo) full of deer and birds. When the Ming built the Forbidden City, they preserved these pleasure gardens, which Yung Lo landscaped and surrounded with walls of imperial purple, and Ch'ien Lung later adorned with

141

temples and pavilions. But above all they are linked with the memory of Tzu Hsi, the dowager empress, who did not much care for the solemn pomp of the Winter Palaces and made these gardens her preferred residence in Peking. She built new palaces and complex pavilions, and passed much of her time there, in her private theater or aboard her pleasure boats, which although not of marble, were very sumptuous. It is said that one evening in 1900, when she was daydreaming on the lake, she suddenly ordered the Boxer leaders to stop their artillery barrage against the foreign barbarians for a while, simply because it was disturbing her. And it was from a raised pavilion to the east of the Nan lake that Tzu Hsi watched the giant fires of June 13, 1900.

The imperial parks are made up of three lakes (*hai*): Pei Hai, the northern lake; Chung Hai, the center lake; and Nan Hai, the southern lake. In the early days of the Republic, Yuan Shi-k'ai took up residence in the palaces of the two southerly lakes, and even today the leaders of the regime have their apartments there. Access to these is forbidden, of course, and only Pei Hai is open to visitors.

Pei Hai

Visits: open daily, until 10 p.m. in winter, 11 p.m. in summer. Entry: 5 fen; free on Sundays.

Is Pei Hai really worth visiting? Some foreigners in Peking shrug their shoulders and cast doubts on Pei Hai's beauty; and it is certainly true that its overcelebrated "Bottle of Peppermint," and the countless little palaces around it on the steep shores of the Island of Hortensias are no more than *chinoiseries* in the most pejorative sense. But there is more than this to Pei Hai. Juliet Bredon, an elderly English lady who adored Peking and who wrote a sympathetic and understanding book about it, wrote these very apt lines: "To analyse the charm of this forgotten corner of Pei Hai, where few visitors penetrate, is impossible. It is a savour that must be tasted, a perfume inhaled, a colour seen with our own eyes. It is in the reflection of willow branches in the lake. It is in the grey stone embankments writhing like dragons along the shores. It is in the flight of ducks towards the south, the song of frogs in the rushes." (*Peking.* Shanghai: Kelley and Walsh, 1922.)

This is the real Pei Hai that you must discover. To do so,

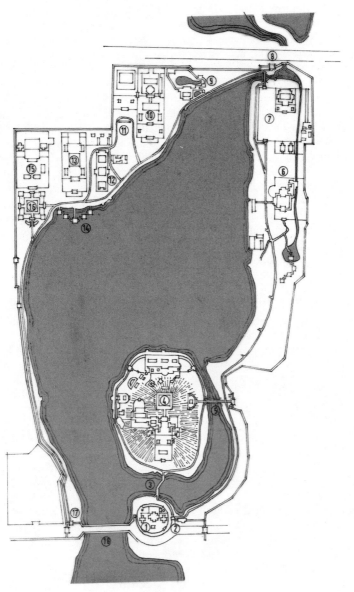

Pei Hai

don't come on a Sunday, for on that day its charm is different
—the charm of a "Peking Sunday" with its docile crowds and
swarming children. And in any case, don't waste much time on
the Island of Hortensias itself; to appreciate a little-known aspect of Pei Hai, start by going around the lake from the east
to the west side.

What to see at Pei Hai (see Plan Number 6):

(1) The *Circular City*, or *Round Tower* (T'uang Ch'eng):
You reach this by a short flight of steps on its west side. This
was the center of the former palace of Kubla Khan, and here
the French novelist Pierre Loti wrote *The Last Days of Peking*.
Its overall charm is due to its lovely cypresses and the deep
shade beneath them, while its special attraction is the black-jade
fountain pool adorned with strange carved dragons which dates
back to the days of the Mongol princes. On the inside of the
pool is inscribed a poem written by Ch'ien Lung to the glory
of wine. A small altar contains a big Buddha in false white
jade.

(2) The main entrance to the park.

(3) The oddly shaped marble bridge with a bend in its
middle.

(4) The *Island of Hortensias* (Ch'ung Hua Tao): We
won't go into too much detail about the forty-nine palaces and
pavilions on this artificial island, which according to legend
was originally a Mongolian mountain transported stone by
stone to Peking in exchange for a T'ang princess! The island
is dominated by the *White Dagoba* (Pai T'a) built by Shun
Chih in 1651 to commemorate the first visit to Peking of the
Dalai Lama of Tibet. On its southern face is an enormous
mystical Tibetan monogram, and the dagoba is described as
follows by Victor Segalen in his novel *René Lys*: "The huge
bulbous hulk of the White Dagoba with its ungainly paunch,
its shape like a Buddhist stupa, its Hindu personality . . .
rather immature! After four millennia of Chinese art and the
authentic cult of the Heavens, the exaggerated piety of this
dagoba seems, like its architecture, too much like *art nouveau*."
Too true.

In front of the dagoba is a statue of the god Yamantaka,
put there to terrify the hostile Mongols.

(5) *Bridge of Perfect Wisdom* (Chih Chu Ch'ia): Beyond
the bridge you follow the path beside the lake. To the right,

on tiny wooded hills, lie scattered pavilions with evocative names—the "Hill of Clouds" or the "House From Where You Can See the Plants Grow."

(6) *Hua Fang Chai*: This group of wooden buildings set around a square pool is unfortunately not open to visitors, but you can get a good view into it from some nearby high ground. The water is black and reflects the fine woodwork of the buildings—woodwork that seems to have been spared the fearful daubing in bright-colored paint that is the fate of many of the tourist sights in present-day Peking.

(7) *Altar of the Silkworms* (Ts'an an Tan) and *Palace of the Empress's silkworms* (Ch'in Ts'an Tien): This former silkworm nursery is also closed to visitors and so, unfortunately, is the temple dedicated to this most precious of the animals of the Chinese Empire. According to legend, it was Hsi Ling, wife of Huang Ti (2600 B.C.), who discovered the silkworm's possibilities.

(8) Northern entry into Pei Hai.

(9) *Garden of Peace of Mind* (Ching Hsin Hai): On this little promontory with its poetic name lie scattered pavilions and pools. Tzu Hsi often used to walk here.

(10) *Little Paradise of the West* (Hsia Hsi Tien): This is made up of two temples, today lived in by the workers who look after the garden. It includes a fine four-story pavilion with yellow and green varnished tiles, built by Ch'ien Lung, and a tall slim pagoda known as the *Pagoda of the Ten Buddhas*.

(11) *Screen of the Nine Dragons* (Chin Lung Pi): This is one of the most celebrated monuments in Peking. It is a polychromatic ceramic wall decorated on both sides with huge dragons. In olden days it stood in front of a temple gate.

(12) *Library of the Hill of Pines*: A pretty enclosure surrounded by pines, formerly approached through a charming ancient gateway but now closed to visitors.

(13) *Temple of Happy Meditation* (Ch'an Fu Sze): A palace for Mao's Young Pioneers; modern, and in bad taste.

(14) *Pavilion of the Five Dragons* (Wu Lung T'ing): This is a suite of five pavilions right by the lake's edge and linked by a series of little bridges. Tourists adore it.

(15) *Grand Paradise of the West* (Ta Hsi Tien): An old temple remarkably restored.

145

THE FACE OF PEKING

(16) *Palace of Kuan Yin* (Kuan Yin Tien): A fine construction in marble and wood, surrounded by a canal crossed by four bridges, in former days it housed hundreds of stucco figurines representing different phases of reincarnation. The statues have disappeared, but the palace is still one of the most handsome wooden buildings in Peking.

(17) Southwest entry to Pei Hai.

(18) *Bridge of Pei Hai*: The most famous bridge in all Peking. Of course it was not opened to the public till after the fall of the Empire, but from the days of Yuan Shi-k'ai it was cut in two, lengthwise, by a wall that concealed from indiscreet eyes the official residences on the banks of Chung Hai and Nan Hai.

Chung Hai and Nan Hai

These two lakes (which are closed to visitors) can be seen only from the marble bridge or from the Hill of Coal or the White Tower. Nonetheless they are famous for several reasons.

On Nan Hai is the *Terrace of the Ocean,* an artificial peninsula made up of palaces and pavilions, where the hapless Kuang Hsu was shut up after 1898. He stayed there ten years, watched over constantly by warders whom Tzu Hsi changed every day. One winter evening he tried to escape by running over the ice, but was quickly caught.

On the west bank of Chung Hai is the *Palace of Brilliant Purple* (Tsu Kuang Ho), built on a terrace of the Ming period. The Manchu kings used it for giving audience to official envoys of foreign powers. Indeed it was here that on June 29, 1873, the emperor received the first European ambassadors to China. Since they refused to prostrate themselves before him, he preferred the ceremony to take place in this out-of-the-way palace, rather than inside the Forbidden City, where he feared losing face in front of the whole world.

Other Parks

Peking has numerous other parks and gardens, some really pleasant, others rather drab, but all having the merit of showing you how the Chinese spend their leisure. Sunday is an astonishing bustle—a Central Park, Hampstead Heath, or Bois de Boulogne reduced to the dimension of a few big gardens. But during the week people sleep on the benches, warm themselves in the sun, play chess, or contemplate the Thought of Mao.

There is one sight not to be missed: early in the morning and late in the afternoon groups of people of all ages invade the gardens to take part in traditional Chinese gymnastic exercises. Their rhythmic hip-swaying seems closer to mime than to Swedish drill, but it develops all the body's muscles and preserves, so it seems, agility of mind. It is amazing to see sturdy housewives and little pigtailed girls practicing side by side the ancient rituals of sword-handling. And if you walk down some out-of-the-way alley, you might come across some old bearded man, wearing a "water-melon" cap dating from his childhood days, practicing all by himself those movements that "rest the soul and revive the body."

Here in my personal order of preference are the main parks of Peking. Usually you must pay a modest entry fee, and they are open till sunset.

Sun Yat-sen park (or Chung Shan park; general map, E5), to the southwest of the Forbidden City, is the most central and so the most accessible of Peking's parks. You must sit here in the shade between rounds of sightseeing, drink a cup of tea, or even take a light meal in the open-air restaurant; there is also a theater. And to the north there is a fine walk, especially pleasant at sunset beside the moats of the Forbidden City.

Tao Jan Ting park (general map, D8). Little known to foreigners, this is one of the pleasantest parks in Peking, enclosing a pretty lake full of tiny islands. Pavilions, palaces, and temples have been turned into teahouses and places for taking a stroll. On Sundays the crowd here is less dense than at Sun Yat-sen, but there is still little chance of being able to rest in the shade.

The Park of the Peoples' Culture (general map, E5), southeast of the Forbidden City (see under Tai Miao in the chapter on temples, pp. 149–168). It is the equivalent in the east of Sun Yat-sen in the west.

Pei Hai (general map, D3) is the most important of Peking parks (see pp. 142).

THE FACE OF PEKING

The Peking Zoo (general map, A2). Its one claim to fame: the pandas, puppylike and charming, that appear on the postage stamps of the Chinese People's Republic. Although the zoo is badly organized, it is really far better stocked with animals than a rapid visit might suggest.

THE TEMPLES OF PEKING

The temples in the heart of the town, harmonious suites of courtyards and palaces, are havens of quiet between gray stone walls; yet the regime regards them as shameful monuments to be hidden from the tourist. The hurried tourist himself doesn't bother much about these temples, though they are an essential part of the charm of Peking. But although the State considers them to be degrading relics of a vanished era and has closed many of them to the public, some can still be visited without too much difficulty. And anyone who wants to gain an idea of the old China and to experience a certain kind of serenity and true beauty should hurry up and visit these temples soon—for in ten or twenty years many will have disappeared and with them the last reminders of distant bygone days.

In former times some sort of religious edifice stood at the corner of almost every street—a modest altar or a sumptuous complex of painted woodwork and glazed tiles. The four Chinese religions coexisted without conflict although "State" temples, dedicated to some official god or other, predominated. Some critics have complained that all the temples are identical, and a certain French count named de Beauvoir, who spent some time in Peking early this century, wrote frankly in his

149

travel book on the city, "I didn't go to see any of them, they are all too ugly." But if the temples of Peking all seem rather similar, except in size, there is a reason: there is a relative unity in the concept of worship common to all Chinese religions (with obscure and terrifying variations in the case of Lamaism), and unity above all in Chinese architecture throughout the ages, whether religious or secular. In any event, to lump them together is to ignore all kinds of details, in the gardens or the sculptures, in the atmosphere of the different temples, and in a mass of curious legends that make up the history of the town. And it is also to forget that in modern Peking three temples in four are out of use or, rather, have been converted into factories or homes. But they are factories and homes that you can visit and where, amid the hurry and bustle of modern China, you can find remarkable vestiges of the past. It is this contrast, this interrelationship of two very different styles of life, that makes up one of the main attractions of the temples of Peking.

How to visit the temples

The Chinese tourist authorities don't much care for one's interest in these "feudal" monuments. And although without your asking for it they will show you the Temple of Heaven, perhaps the Tai Miao (or Temple of Ancestors, today a cultural center), and the so-called Temple of the Lamas, in the case of the other interesting temples things are rather different. So you have two possible methods of approach. In the first, you tell the China Travel Service of your wish to see certain temples; depending on the circumstances, on your own personality, and on the spirit of initiative of the man behind the counter, you will get either a "yes" or a "no." If it is a "no," don't be discouraged, for there is a fair chance that you'll be able to see the temples on your own account, and so you must try the second approach: guidebook in hand, and perhaps with the help of a taxi, set off on your adventure. And you won't regret it.

But as it is not so easy to find one's way around Peking, the map on page 153 may be helpful. If you get lost, just try talking Chinese: repeat three or four times to the first passer-by the name of the temple you want; he will be flabbergasted by your knowledge and will certainly help you.

Page 1. Showcase of the system, the Museum of the Revolution, is on T'ien An Men Square, ceremonial center of China (Top). So is the Gate of Heavenly Peace, entrance to the Imperial Palace (Bottom). *Pages 2 and 3*. The Forbidden City complex is made up of two groups of three palaces each. The *T'ai Ho Tien* is the first of the front palaces. (Photos: *Marc Riboud*/Magnum) *Page 4*. The Temple of Heaven, the most famous in all China, is actually a triumphal avenue with three terrace-temples rising from it. (Photo: *René Burri*/Magnum)

Above. Outside Peking: The Boat of Marble, one of the many "Chinoiserie" props of the New Summer Palace. *Next Page.* A masterpiece of classical Chinese functional architecture, the Marco Polo Bridge has 280 lions standing guard over its 12 marble arches. (Photos: *Marc Riboud*/Magnum)

The triumphal road leading to the thirteen Ming Dynasty Tombs. The extraordinary "Alley of the Animals" displays twelve pairs of marble animals and four pairs of warriors and ministers. (Photos: *René Burri*/Magnum)

Wan Li Chan Chen, the colossal Wall of the Ten Thousand Li, is only a few hours' drive from the capital. (Photo: *Marc Riboud/ Magnum*)

THE TEMPLES OF PEKING

But you won't be able to see all the temples a
as it may seem, there is no book that lists them sys
The following is a rapid description of those temp...
exist and can, in one way or another, be visited, and that are
worth a trip through the streets of Peking.

Easy guide to a Chinese Temple

Before beginning your adventure, it is best to have some
general ideas on Chinese temples. First you will notice, from
the names of the buildings, that there are at least five different words in Chinese that mean "temple," each with its
own separate significance:

Most temples are *Sze*, which means they are Buddhist.

The *Kuan* are Taoist temples.

The name *Miao* is given to former official State temples
and, by extension, to temples in general.

The *Kung* are Lamaist temples.

The name *Tien* means "palace," but can also refer to the
main hall of a temple.

Nearly all Chinese temples are built on a strictly uniform
pattern (map Number 7 is simply an example, not relating
to any specific building but applicable to three-quarters of the
city's temples).

The entrance to each temple is screened by a wall that keeps
out evil spirits. Immediately beyond this wall is a *pai-lou*
through which you pass into a first courtyard. Buddhist
temples are always aligned from south to north. To the left
and right of the entrance are two pavilions, called "towers,"
one housing a clock and the other a huge drum—ritual instruments out of use today even in those temples still used for
worship. In the two opposite corners of the first courtyard
there may be two further pavilions, containing steles often
standing on statues of turtles or dragons. Then you pass
through another gateway, which is really a building in itself,
guarded by one or two pairs of gigantic grinning statues. From
here you go into another courtyard, and then one, two, three,
or four more, each one enclosed on the north side by a temple
dedicated to some divinity or holy man. The central temple
may have one or even two upper floors and will contain a
huge Buddha. In each courtyard there are steles, huge bronze
bowls, and incense-burners on tripods. On either side of the

main temple, to east and west, are the libraries, refectories, and dormitories for the monks, and other annexes.

You can take photographs to your heart's content, both inside and outside the temples—the changeless smiles of the Buddhas and the Taoist saints are impervious to flashbulbs. If for one reason or another it seems you are being banned from a temple, don't make a fuss but come back next day.

The Major Temples of Peking

There are some monuments that simply *must* be seen and others that it is simply pleasant to have seen. In the first group are three temples very different from each other.

The Temple of Heaven (Number 1 on the general map; see also Plan Number 8). You leave the Tartar City by Ch'ien Men and follow the wide avenue toward the south as far as the Bridge of Heaven, where you turn left. From Ch'ien Men to the Temple of Heaven is several miles and you should take a taxi or a pedicab.

The Temple of Heaven, the most famous in Peking and in all China, is one of the wonders of the world and deserves a detailed description.

It is not really a temple in the classic sense of the word. It is a triumphal avenue eight hundred yards long with three terraces rising from it: *The Temple of the Annual Prayer* (Ch'i Nien Tien), *The Temple of the God of the Universe* (Huang Ch'ung Yu), and *The Altar of Heaven* (Tien Tan). Here we are far from the classic plan of the typical temple already described. But this is a rare exception in Peking—save for the altars of the Earth, Moon, and Sun, respectively to the north, west, and east of the Tartar City.

This temple is also a unique and privileged spot. Every year, at the moment of the winter solstice, the emperor came here to make solemn sacrifice. This ceremony dates back to prehistoric days, but its deeper significance is strangely akin to Judeo-Christian doctrine. In his role of "Son of Heaven" the sovereign took upon himself the sins of all his people—that is, of all humanity—and prostrated and humiliated himself, offering himself as a kind of sacrifice to his Father, for the redemption of mankind. For this he put on a costume of dark blue and quit the imperial palaces on the eve of the holy day, escorted by soldiers and officials, by musicians, and by princes

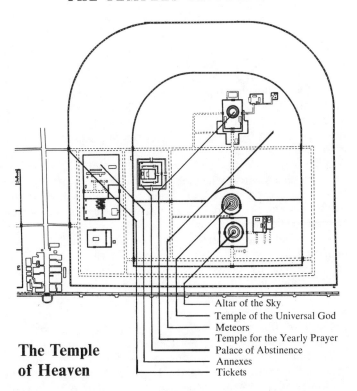

**The Temple
of Heaven**

Altar of the Sky
Temple of the Universal God
Meteors
Temple for the Yearly Prayer
Palace of Abstinence
Annexes
Tickets

of the blood royal. Every gate and every window overlooking his route had to be closed tight, from the gate of Ch'ien Men to the entrance to the sacred precinct. Above all, no foreigner was allowed to watch the procession pass, and foreign diplomats were officially advised to stay in their quarters that day. It even happened that the train from Tientsin (once the line was open) was forced to a standstill for forty-eight hours, in order not to disturb the silence of the ceremony.

Let us visit the Temple of Heaven by following the same path as the emperor. First there were preliminary halts in the splendid side buildings, which today have been turned into a barracks, a radio station, and an open-air theater. The emperor then went to the Temple of the God of the Universe. You will have come thus far by car, which will drop you at the foot of the huge terrace rising some feet above the gardens.

153

The Temple of the God of the Universe is on the right, that is, toward the south. In front of it is a fine gateway and around it a precinct with its entrance also to the south. You can see the temple elegantly framed in the arch of the gateway. It is a circular pavilion overlooking a marble terrace and is covered with tiles of a lovely deep blue. There are a number of possible echo effects, which always amuse Chinese visitors—and if it amuses you too to whisper against the wall of the temple's precinct and be heard by someone standing against the wall, but at the other end, you can always do so.

After burning a few sticks of incense before the memorial steles of his ancestors, the emperor moved toward the Temple of Annual Prayer, which can be reached by going back northward from the first temple and passing through the gateways at either end of the sacred way.

This Temple of Annual Prayer is quite marvelous. It is a high building covered with a three-tiered roof, also in blue tiles, first built by Yung Lo and later repaired several times—Ch'ien Lung noted that it was falling into ruins and had it almost entirely rebuilt, but it was damaged by fire in 1899. So the temple you see today is "modern," but in terms of Chinese art this matters little: it is the exact replica of what it was five centuries ago. You reach it by a beautiful three-level circular terrace. The sun shines down on the marble balustrades, casting shadows on the worn steps, and the light is always more lovely here than anywhere else in Peking. It was here that the emperor spent a night of fasting and prayer.

In the morning he went back along the path he had taken the day before, passing the Temple of the God of the Universe and finally reaching the Altar of Heaven. Three terraces, that of man, of the earth, and of heaven, rise concentrically, surrounded by three balustrades of 360 pillars, in the form of a kind of altar, perfectly flat and round, where the emperor was perhaps closer to Heaven than any other mortal had ever been. We know in detail the ceremony that then took place, we know the place of each person, of each sacred utensil. While the incense was burning, while a whole ox was being sacrificed, and scrolls of silk unrolled, priests recited ancient prayers in loud voices. The Son of Heaven, immobile, hieratic, went into a kind of holy ecstacy. It was the supreme moment of his reign on earth, the moment that justified it. Musicians played on traditional instruments in a syncopated rhythm that intensified at the key moments of the ceremony. No other drama of ancient days can have had a more intense emotional impact.

Climb onto the highest terrace, imagine the mimes and the dancers, the noise of worship and its reverberating rhythms: such is the secret memory of a China that vanished in 1911. When Yuan Shi-k'ai took power, he tried to imitate the rites of the emperors he had helped to overthrow, but it was a feeble parody.

Today the Temple of Heaven is open to all. It includes a kind of snack bar or tea garden, but has not lost its nobility. The Chinese government keeps it in good condition and charges a 10-fen entrance fee. If you can, go back several times. It is beautiful on early winter mornings and equally so in the heat of high summer, when it becomes a mosaic of different shades of blue.

There is not much point in going to see the so-called meteorites in the park: they are big stones, obviously sculpted with a mallet and neither authentic nor interesting.

The Temple of the Ancestors (Tai Miao; today, Wen Hua Kung; general map, Number 2, E5—to the right of T'ien An Men, on Ch'ang An). Tai Miao used to be one of the loveliest and most classic temples in Peking, but it has been deconsecrated and turned into exhibition halls to become *The Palace of the Workers' Culture.*

Tai Miao dates back to 1420, when the capital of China was removed from Nanking to Peking. Built to house the tablets of the ancestors of Yung Lo, it was burned down in 1464 and rebuilt in the same style. In their turn the Manchu used it to honor their ancestors—once they had carefully burned the tablets of the previous dynasty.

You can still see what Tai Miao must have been like. The buildings, in a square precinct set in the heart of the Park of Culture, are surrounded by fine cedars that provide an atmosphere of shade and calm. After passing through a first gate, decorated with ceramics, you find the central palaces of the temple. The former *Temple of the Joyous Sacrifice* (Chien Tien), on a raised terrace decorated with huge chimeras, is elegant: although monolithic, it is harmonious, and its roofs appear a good deal loftier than those of most of the other temples. Alas, it has just been daubed over with fearful red *sang-de-boeuf* paint, and the timberwork beams are painted in just those shades of blue and green that affront the eyes at the Summer Palace.

The second building was called the *Central Palace* (Chung Tien), and the last, reached after going through yet one more gate, was the *Temple of Ancestors* itself, the Tiao Tien. The rich interior decorations have all disappeared, and in the central palace people are playing Ping-Pong. . . .

Go into the last enclosure: you are now facing the southeast moat of the Forbidden City. Beyond rise the City's crenellated walls, while near you lovers sit on the benches, and punts and barges move on the waters of the moat. This too is Peking.

The Temple of the Lamas (Yung Ho Kung—Palace of Concord and harmony; general map, Number 3, G1). This is one of the most impressive of Peking's temples. Until the end of 1964 all you had to do to visit it was push open the gate and walk in, but now you must ask permission at the tourist office.

It is a fairly new temple. Until the middle of the eighteenth century it was a princely residence, which Ch'ien Lung rebuilt in 1745 and devoted to the cult of the living Lama. From then on and almost up to the Communist seizure of power, dark rumors were current about this temple—tales were told of kidnaped tourists, while Arlington recounted in his book *In Search of Old Peking* that he had had to whip out a revolver to make his escape from some particularly dangerous monks. Until 1966 the temple was inhabited by fifty monks and lay brothers, dressed in brown-serge robes. You could still take part in the morning service, a daily ritual similar to that at Lhasa. The strange rites celebrated there at certain times of the year under the name of "Dance of the Devil" were not discontinued until 1959.

The halls and courtyards of the Temple of the Lamas are built according to the most orthodox plan. It is advisable to go through them slowly, for they include some odd things. In the side halls are extraordinary figures of the gods of Tibet—monstrous deities with several arms apiece, wearing necklaces of tiny death's heads and sitting astride mules or oxen. Some are clasping naked women in a most suggestive manner. The most obscene of these figurines, known as "Buddhas of joy," were formerly shown (as at Pompeii) to visitors who asked to see them—but they had to pay a lot for a look. Today the puritanical Chinese regime lets you see only some of the less offensive; the rest are carefully swathed in yellow sheets—but the more understanding monks can be persuaded to lift a corner of the veil.

The temple contains other marvels: Tibetan paintings, huge frescoes, precious statues—the resemblance of certain ancient Buddhas to Queen Victoria is astonishing!—as well as Ninghsia carpets, seventeenth-century cloisonnés, and, in the central pavilion, a beautiful figure of Buddha. But the most famous statue is a colossal "Buddha yet to come," the Messiah of the Lamas, whose head and shoulders disappear into the upper floors of the rear pavilion. This building is remarkable in style: it is linked to the two side wings of the temple by aerial corridors of amazing lightness. The roofs of the temple are also very fine.

Before leaving the temple, try to imagine it as it once was, with its monks in their yellow vestments, their headdresses like Phrygian helmets, the long ceremonial trumpets, and the Superior of the monastery uttering terrible incantations:

O Sor, who changes the fishermen to dust,
O Sor, who changes to dust the impious enemies of the faith,
I, the Yogatsari, appeal to the Sor,
To the dread Sor, sharper than the spear,
And more powerful even than thunder!

The Other Temples of Peking

It is in trying to visit the other temples that you may sometimes have difficulties. But don't despair: people may look at you suspiciously as you clamber over barbed wire to reach the remains of some former sanctuary, but no one will stop you; and if the temple in question has become a factory or youth hostel, ask at the gate for permission to enter. If necessary, get your taxi-driver to help you, or the obliging local inhabitant who has been guiding you through the maze of little streets. Two times out of three you will get in.

THE FACE OF PEKING

The temples of the Tartar City.

Five little temples in the Imperial City: These five temples set around the Forbidden City unfortunately cannot be visited, but from the outside you can see their beautiful roofs and discern the general layout of their rooms. As you will probably come across them, you may as well know what they are.

(1) *Lei Shen Miao* (Temple of the God of Thunder; general map, Number 4, D4), west of Pei Ch'ang Chieh. To this temple, built in 1732 by Yeng Cheng, all the officials of the Court went on the first day of the second and eighth months to pray and offer sacrifice.

(2) *Hsing Lung Sze* (Temple of Prosperity; general map, Number 5, D4), north of the above on the same side of the avenue. This former armory dating back to the days of Yung Lo contains a statue of Lu Pan, the god of architects. In 1700 K'ang Hsi made it into a temple.

(3) Fu Yu Sze (Temple of Blessed Protection; general map, Number 6, D4) is on the east side of Pei Ch'ang Chieh, facing the temple above. Built by Yung Chen in 1723, here the Emperor came to work and read his letters. For a while the premises housed the services of the Panchen Lama, later transferred to Ku Lou Hsi Ta Chieh (plan, D2).

(4) *Feng Shen Miao* (Temple of the God of the Winds; general map, Number 7, E4) is to the east of Pei Chih Tse. Another important official temple, once frequented by the officials of the Court, it was built in 1728 on the orders of Ch'ien Lung.

(5) *Yun Shen Miao* (Temple of the God of Clouds; general map, Number 8, E4) is to the south of the above, on the same side of the avenue. It was also built by Ch'ien Lung.

The Three in One (general map, Number 9, E3) are at the end of the only *hutung* on Chingshan Chien Chieh, between Chingshan Tung Ta Chieh and Huangcheng Ken. This curious group of three temples, worth a visit that might turn out to be quite adventurous, were lived in by Mongol lamas who printed sacred Mongol and Tibetan books for Peking. Today the *Chi Chu Sze* (Temple of Knowledge), to the west, is a school. The *Sung Chu Sze* (Temple of the Sacrifice to the Mountain) is a factory. And the *Fa Yuan Sze* (Temple of the Exaltation of Buddha), on the east, is a real microcosm of

158

all Peking. The palaces of the temple are simultaneously a workshop (workers are busy everywhere), a school (you can peer into classrooms), and dwellings (nearly a hundred families live in the monks' small cells, half in the open air). Visit the Fa Tuan Sze on a summer's evening and you will see a side of Peking life that is little known.

Mahakala Miao (Mongol Temple) or P'u Tu Sze (Temple of the Savior of the Universe; general map, Number 10, E4) is in the last *hutung* to the east of Nan Chitse. It is one of the strangest and most imposing buildings in Peking, dating back to the early fifteenth century. It was originally an imperial palace, then a Lamaist temple from 1691. It was inhabited by Mongol monks and contained a huge statue of Mahakala, the savior of the universe, a god of terrifying aspect. You cannot get inside the temple, but you can easily walk around its outside. It is a huge colonnaded palace set on a massive brick terrace, its façade decorated with a curious row of double projecting roofs, and it overlooks a sea of *hutung* and little gray houses.

The White Pagoda (Pai Ta Sze; general map, Number 11, C3), north of Fu Cheng Men Ta Chieh, stands on a main street and is a kind of village within the city, as well as a very fine temple. Built by Kubla Khan, who was particularly interested in Lamaist religious rites, it is in the style of a Mongol stupa, consisting of a circular white tower crowned with a flat sheet of copper from which were hung a thousand tiny bells. It was restored by Yung Lo, then by Ch'ien Lung. According to legend, when it was on the point of collapsing, the god of architects, Lu Pan, intervened personally to save it from ruin. It has remained just as it was seven hundred years ago, a distinguished stranger to the usual style of Peking. Around it were built several altars and temple halls, one of which, the rear pavilion, you can still visit if you search in the precinct for the old monk who looks after it. The other buildings have been colonized by a teeming mass of squatters, who dry their linen on lines stretched between the varnished roofs and do their cooking outdoors in the bronze pots once used for offertories. During your visit you will be followed by children and youths, happy and curious to see a foreign face—and today a remarkable cheerfulness reigns over this former spiritual center of the lamas' cult.

Li Tai Ti Wang Miao (Temple of Succeeding Generations of Emperors; general map, 12, C3) is north of Fu Cheng Men Ta Chieh. For a long time it has not been possible to visit this huge temple, which was built in 1523 to house the tablets of all the emperors (including those of past dynasties) except usurpers, tyrants, and enemies of the arts—Kubla Khan's tablets were removed by Chie Ching only to be replaced by K'ang Hsi. The Li Tai Ti Wang Miao is today a school, but you can walk around the front courtyard.

Kuang Chi Sze (Temple of Universal Charity; general map, Number 13, C3), north of Fu Cheng Men Ta Chieh, is today the most important Buddhist temple in Peking, but there is little left to be seen in it. You will be shown its palaces and the monks' quarters. Once it housed a fine library but this was dispersed a long time ago. Note the fresco that the artist painted with his fingers, without the help of brushes and in a strange primitive style.

Ching Yeh Sze (Temple of Serene Study; general map, Number 14, C1), on the north bank of Hsi Hai, is now the home of several families. This little temple is nevertheless worth a visit, for it is set on a small hill that affords a marvelous view over the northern lakes of Peking. The origin of Ching Yeh Sze is uncertain, but it was restored by Ch'ien Lung and once contained a stele that enjoined the Buddhist monks to practice humility. There is still a fine marble stele in front of the temple.

Kuang Hua Sze (Temple of Religious Transformation; general map, Number 15, D2), which lies between the southern part of Hou Hai and Ku Lou Hsi Ta Chieh, is a Buddhist temple still in use. If you can cajole the monk, who may hesitate to let you in, you will be able to visit at least part of it and perhaps see the numerous clocks, statues, and steles from other temples now destroyed. Kuang Hua Sze owes its name to the miracle by which a certain monk transformed the pittance of alms he received, rice grain by rice grain, into a magnificent temple.

Temple of Confucius and *Hall of Classics* (Kung Miao and Kuo Tze Chien; general map, Number 16, F1) are in the Ch'eng Hsieh Chieh *hutung* on the Yung Ho King Ta Chieh, facing the Temples of the Lamas. The Temple of Confucius is still in perfect condition, but an attempt to visit it usually provokes problems, if not an outright refusal, because it has become a school for executives of the Chinese Communist Party. However, its role in Peking's history and art history has been so important that it must be described. And as for the Hall of Classics next door, the tourist office will gladly let you in.

The Temple of Confucius was originally built by Yuan Chih Ching, then restored by K'ang Hsi and Ch'ien Lung. It was less a place of worship than a garden of meditation, where sacrificial rites in honor of the Master were also performed. On the twenty-seventh day of the eighth month an important "State" ceremony took place there. This ceremony became such an integral part of the customs of the Chinese leaders that after a break of twenty years, following the fall of the Empire, it was started up again in 1934 in the presence of the city's leading officials.

In order to prove their humility toward Confucius, all the officials who visited his temple had to get down from their palanquins before entering. There is a legend that one proud man who refused to obey this rule was struck by a branch that fell suddenly from a tree and crushed the chair in which he was being carried.

In addition to various statues and steles, the Kung Miao formerly contained the ten stone Chou "drums," the oldest existing Chinese sculptures, now exhibited in the museum of drums in the Forbidden City (see p. 132).

The Hall of Classics, west of the Temple of Confucius, was a sort of national library where inscriptions on stone, the principal classical Chinese texts, were kept. It was hoped that putting them in this library would prevent China's literary heritage from disappearing if some monarch were ever to repeat the gesture of Shih Huang-ti, who in 213 B.C. staged a burning of the books (see p. 20). A school for studying the Confuc'... ts was later established here. The hall is made up of sevₑ al buildings surrounding a courtyard, where a fine circular pavilion stands on a terrace in the middle of a "circular river." Here the emperor came in humility to learn the teachings of Confucius.

The Temples of the Chinese City.

Many of these are among the oldest religious buildings in Peking. On the whole they were less well kept up and restored than the others, and it is also these that have suffered most under the new regime. I shall describe nine of them—there used to be hundreds—but only four can really be visited. You can see the others from outside, and perhaps get in—as I did—by asking a special favor, but mostly they are now schools, offices, or factories.

Pao Kuo Sze (Temple of the Recognition of the State; general map, Number 17, B6) is to the north of Kuang An Min Ta Chieh. It dates back to the Chou and is considered one of the oldest temples in Peking. Several times restored, it is still today a fine ensemble of palaces strictly confined within an enclosure of red walls. In theory it is not open to visitors, but you can easily get into the first courtyard.

Ch'ang Ch'un Sze (Temple of Eternal Spring; general map, Number 18, B6) is to the west of Hsia Hsieh Chieh. The mother of Wan Li, who had sworn to devote her son to the service of Buddha, had this temple built in 1560 to house a young monk whom she put on the throne in place of the young emperor. Today the temple is a dispensary and you can enter it.

Ch'ing Chen Sze (mosque; general map, Number 19, B7) is to the east of Niu Chieh, the "Street of the Cow"—so called because the butchers here, in the heart of the Moslem quarter, sold no pork. There is little apparent difference between the great mosque of Niu Chieh and any Chinese temple: it has a pai-lou in front of it and a multicolored pavilion, and contains various other pavilions that look entirely Buddhist. But the main hall is long and bare, divided into naves by several pillars and decorated with various Arab characters. You can visit it easily and will be warmly welcomed by the elderly Moslems who maintain it.

Kuan Yin Sze (Temple of Yuan Yin; general map, Number 20, D6) is in the extension of Ta Sha La. It is a typical little local temple, dedicated to Kuan Yin, the goddess of mercy, and today is closed.

The Temples of Ch'ien Men (general map, Number 21, E6): these two little temples, now at one end of the public garden of Ch'ien Men, are perfect examples of the temples formerly within the enclosure of each gate of the city. Their function was to protect the entrances to the town. The two temples of Ch'ien Men were dedicated to the god of war (Kuan Ti) and the goddess of mercy (Kuan Yin). When Tzu Hsi came back from exile in 1901, she made a halt at the Kuan Ti Miao.

THE TEMPLES OF PEKING

Ching Chung Miao (Temple of the Knight Loyal to the Very End; general map, Number 22, E7) is at the northwest corner of the lake of the golden fish. The temple was dedicated by Ch'ien Lung to a Chinese national hero, Yueh Fei. Unfortunately it has been converted—into a sponge factory!

Pan Tao Kung (Temple of the Peach Trees of Paradise; general map, Number 23, G6) is in the northeast corner of the Chinese City, beside the moats of the Tartar City. Once a year—on the third day of the third moon—this temple was visited by young girls about to marry. Today it is a factory, but you can go around it, and it offers a fine view over the Tower of the Fox.

Fa Ta Sze (The Tired Little Pagoda; general map, Number 24, G7) is just before the level crossing on Tso An Men Ta Chieh. It used to stand in the middle of a temple, and the legend about it is quaint: A little pagoda in Mongolia one day decided to see the Forbidden City. So it set off, and went on walking for years, but when it reached Peking at last, it was too exhausted to pass through the ramparts of the Chinese City, and where it stopped it stayed. It is small and pretty, ten stories high, and dates from the time of Yung Lo.

Fa Yuan Sze (Temple of the Origins of the Law; general map, Number 27, C7), the largest Buddhist temple in the Chinese City, is rather hard to find, in a *hutung* to the north of Nan Heng Chieh. To visit it you need an official permit, which is not often granted. For a very long time Fa Yuan Sze has been a kind of seminary, the only center for advanced religious studies in all China. Although much restored, it is an elegant building. Especially worth looking at are the rear courtyards, and the network of galleries and stairways of the central temple (from which you get a fine view over the inner courts). It houses numerous Buddhist treasures, such as Ming paintings, and splendid blue-and-white vases—but perhaps the place is a little too like a museum. In spring its famous lilacs are in flower. It is worth noting that in 1965 this unique religious school had only eighty students.

The Temple of Agriculture (general map, Number 28, D8) is one of the greatest temples in Peking, but the Chinese authorities do not allow visits. Here the emperor used to come amid great pomp, during the third lunar month, to perform ancient and holy rites as in the Temple of Heaven, which is quite nearby. Surrounded by all the members of the Court, he personally cultivated a little patch of earth, tracing out with a gilded plow eight furrows from east to west. Behind him came various officials who ceremoniously sowed corn and four different types of millet. The imperial harvest from this field were gathered in autumn to be used for certain sacrifices. Besides several palaces the huge precinct of the Temple of Agriculture includes a square terrace in white marble "from where people watch the plowing."

The Temples Outside the Walls.

Just outside the ramparts are the inner suburbs of Peking, which teem with picturesque and valuable temples. But many of them are hard to find because today they have been swallowed up by new housing. The plans and directions given below may help you.

North of the town. *Yellow Temple* (Hoang Sze; leave the town by Teh Sheng Men and after about a mile, before you get to the east-west ring road, take an unpaved road to the right). This is one of the most interesting temples in the suburbs, and owes its name to the Indian-style stupa, topped with gilded copper, that stands inside it. The temple was built in 1651 to house the Dalai Lama on his visits to Peking; the stupa dates from 1781. The temple's history is one of repeated mutilation and desecration, but it has been amazingly well restored. You approach it through a heavy red door that bears a notice in large Chinese lettering, "Do Not Enter." As you don't speak Chinese, just carry on, and an old woman will run up to you with little cries, not to chase you away but to make you sign a visitors' book that is probably in reality a police register—you can write in it what you like.

The temple is made up of three courtyards leading to a terrace on which stands the fine stupa, consisting of a thirty-foot-high central tower flanked by four little circular towers decorated with sculptures depicting scenes from the life of Buddha. As a whole the temple has a melancholy air, but in the lamas' former cells live little old men, bearded and smiling, who are only too keen to enter into long conversations.

Near the Yellow Temple there used to be a curious building, the *Tsan Tan*, or Temple of Meditation, a sort of open-roofed mortuary where the bodies of dead lamas were kept for a time in wooden coffins. Every year the coffins were nailed up and sent off to somewhere in Tibet. Old residents of Peking remember having visited this Lamaist funeral parlor.

Altar of the Earth (Ti Tan; immediately on the right after An Ting Men). This corresponds on the north side of town to the Temple of Heaven on the south, but today there are only a few traces left of what must have been an imposing building. Surprisingly, anyone can go in, for it is both a hospital and a training center for Young Pioneers. The altar itself has disappeared, but to the south of the principal corridor you can still see the slaughterhouses where sacrificial animals were executed. But its fine roofs have been damaged and its walls mutilated. Near the entrance and to the north of the main corridor you can see the whole ensemble of the courtyards and palaces of the temple, where the priests gathered before officiating at the holy altar. The roofs are among the finest in Peking, but the whole place is overhung with trees and foliage and swarms with children in red scarves.

Temple of the Large Clock (Ta Chung Sze; see Plan Number 9: north of the main east-west ring road to the north of Peking). This was once a flourishing temple, at whose annual fair horse-racing was organized. Today you can visit only its rear pavilion, which contains the clock that gives the temple its name. The rest is a factory and closed to visitors—a pity, for the roofs are beautiful and well preserved. To get inside, you follow the natural lake that flanks it to the east of the ramparts as far as the northern end, where a small gate remains open. Children play in the mud, or on the ice in winter, while women gather scraps of coal slag—the area is sad and depressing. But the one courtyard open to visitors is fine, and includes several steles dating back to the last years of the Ming. The clock pavilion is closed by a wooden gate decorated with a geometric fretwork design, and someone will unbolt it for you so that you can get to the clock, a fine bronze object twenty feet high and weighing fifty tons. Inscribed on it, both inside and outside, is the whole of the *Fa Hua Sutra*, one of the sacred Buddhist books. If you insist, the monk who is showing you around will fetch a key and unlock a huge piece of wood that he swings to and fro several times before striking the bronze clock with it. The sound is deep and resonant.

165

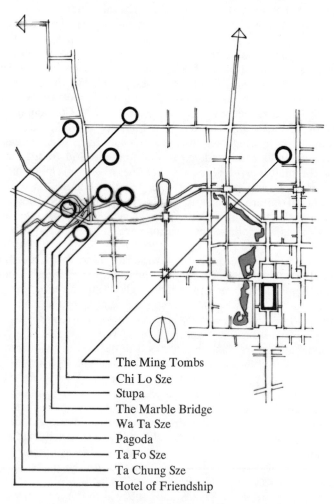

The Ming Tombs
Chi Lo Sze
Stupa
The Marble Bridge
Wa Ta Sze
Pagoda
Ta Fo Sze
Ta Chung Sze
Hotel of Friendship

Northwest Suburb of Peking

THE TEMPLES OF PEKING

West of the Town. *Wu Ta Sze* (Temple of the Five Pagodas; see Plan Number 9). You get to this by following the western bank of the river which crosses a marble bridge on the road to the Summer Palace. The temple is a massive Indian-style building crowned by five pyramids of white marble. It commemorates the visit to Peking of a Hindu nobleman named Pantita, who presented Yung Lo with a reproduction of the famous throne of Buddha that marks the spot where the saint was touched by grace. In return, the emperor offered his guest a plot of land and the means to build on it an enlarged replica of his gift: the Wu Ta Sze. Today this throne of Buddha stands empty in a deserted enclosure—but you should imagine it as it used to be, rising above the curving roofs of the temples and the gold of the glazed tiles.

Ta Fo Sze (Temple of the Great Buddha; Plan Number 9). It is not easy to find the remains of this temple (also known as *Ta Hui Sze*), which today is in the middle of a vast building site, gradually being submerged by apartments and factories. You can, however, reach it by looking out for its roof of glazed tiles, then following the unpaved track that leads to it from the road of the Hotel of Friendship. The temple is in the middle of a factory and only the central pavilion has been preserved. This contains an extraordinary collection of grinning, painted gods, each twenty to thirty feet high. Wild beasts and wise old men surround a Buddha who has ten arms and is escorted by four servants.

Chi Lo Sze (Temple of Supreme Happiness; Plan Number 9): You can see this to the north of the Wu Ta Sze. And that's about all you can see of it, for this ancient temple, which dates back to the thirteenth century and once enclosed a little pagoda, has become a very ugly factory.

Po Yun Kuan (Temple of the White Clouds; Number 25 on the general map, A5): This ancient T'ang temple, rebuilt by Genghis Khan, lies just to the west of the northern part of the Chinese City ramparts. For a long time it was the only official Taoist temple in modern Peking, and a visit to it is rather interesting. It includes genuine "popular art" treasures, coming mostly from the Tung Yueh Miao, a Taoist temple to the east of Peking ransacked in 1949. Note especially the vases, tripods, and incense-burners, and the Taoist divinatory emblems made of three horizontal bars, some of them divided into sections embodying masculine and feminine principles. The last palace before the rear one is dedicated to the blessed Chu Ch'i, a saintly monk whose body lies under a curious vase made from a single root. The rear building is a three-story temple where effigies of all the Taoist gods are preserved.

Tien Ning Sze (Temple of Heavenly Peace; Number 26 on the general map, A6) is just south of the Po Yun Kuan, and from far off you can see the fourteen stories of its pagoda. With a bit of parleying, you can probably succeed in getting inside the precinct of the temple, which has now become a factory. The pagoda, one of the finest monuments in Peking and falling gently into ruin, stands on an octagonal base decorated with sixteen giant Sung statues, four of which are still more or less intact—two are grinning guardians and two, goddesses of great beauty. Although the Tien Ning Sze has been atrociously mutilated and degraded, you should go and see it before there is nothing left at all.

And there are many more ruined temples around Peking, some just walls or a glazed roof here and there, transformed into a school or factory. Walk around the outside of the ramparts and you will see steles and remains of palaces. You may stumble upon an urn of white marble on a piece of waste-land, or statues standing in the middle of fields of corn. Go closer to them and you will come near to the heart of the life of modern China, which has set up its volleyball nets and grain silos in the temples and palaces. What you will see is nothing in comparison to what has disappeared: the walls of the great *Tung Yueh Miao* are still standing, but there are no traces of the Altar of the Moon or of the Sun, while the "iron pagoda" has been razed to the ground like so many others, and soon even their names will have been forgotten.

THE DISTRICTS AND STREETS
OF PEKING

To see the real Peking, take to the streets. The Forbidden City or the Temple of Heaven may represent Chinese art in its most perfect form—but after all, this is no longer the real China. For that you must go to the countryside and to the city streets.

First you see the Chinese crowds, different from one hour to another, one day to another, one month to another. In winter men and women are uniformly clothed in several thicknesses of cotton suits sewn one onto the other, or else in long shaggy untanned skins, knotted and laced up to make them look like rolypoly padded figures.

In summer the thick clothes disappear, and shorts and light shirts replace the classic blue or khaki tunics. Faces are more smiling and relaxed. On Sundays, the streets are thick with families—window-shopping, sucking ices, or munching fritters. In contrast, on weekdays the streets are relatively deserted until nightfall—save for the children, and Peking swarms with them. They play in the yellow dust, their backsides naked to the air because their parents take the precaution of dressing them, summer and winter alike and until they are quite old, in trousers with slits that open of their own accord when necessary. Then around 6 or 7 p.m. the adults reappear in the streets, and with their bicycle bells ringing, they invade the main avenues and the little *hutung*.

You can observe the Peking street traders—the itinerant vendors of fritters, fried pancakes, steamed rolls, and candy-coated "red fruit." You can hear the vendors raucously hawking their wares and see the docile lines of children waiting their turn, each with a few fen in his hand. In winter, coal, and in summer, cabbages are sold in the streets. There are the restaurants spilling out onto the pavements, the countless open-air cookshops of Peking, the libraries also open to the street, where children and adults sit side by side on little benches, reading educational comic strips or from the *Selected Works of Mao Tse-tung*. In the teahouses people sip their jasmine tea despite the efforts of the regime to abolish such moments of idleness; and squatting in the corner of some gateway old men play Chinese chess.

You can see the houses of Peking. First, the former upper-class homes of the smart suburbs: all you will see of these today are great red gateways (but behind their closed walls are series of courtyards surrounded by verandas) and roofs similar in structure but infinitely varied in decoration. You can see the curved tiles along the ridges of the roofs, the lintels of the gateways, and the fine sculptures set between the tiles and the upper limit of the walls. You can also see the poor houses of the workers' districts, with their exterior woodwork, low doors, and oiled-paper windows. You can see ᴛ shops with their flamboyant façades, their pediments decorated with carved lions or dragons; and the little shops not very different from the street stalls of medieval Europe.

Finally you can see the streets themselves: wide, serene, tree-lined avenues; and the alleyways, narrow *hutung*, where water trickles in the dust and where sometimes a solitary tree blocks the way and forces you to detour.

This is the Peking that should be seen. But to see it, you must leave the great boulevards such as Wan Fu Ching or Ch'ang An Chieh and dare to venture beyond the district of the antique shops. Here are a few districts and a few streets for you to sample.

In fact there are two Pekings, two different universes separated by Ch'ien Men, the "Front Gate": to the north lies the Tartar City and to the south the Chinese City.

The Tartar City is the former aristocratic quarter, where princes, men of letters, and officials lived. True, there were slums in the Tartar City, but in general this was the "fashionable" area. The houses were built in regular order on traditional models, and the smart dwellings differed from the poorer ones only in size. The Chinese City, by contrast, was inhabited by working people and the new-rich, the merchants. Hence in the Chinese City there is more variety in the buildings: shops are much more numerous, and here you find ornate façades with Chinese motifs and narrow streets full of commerce. Beyond Ch'ien Men it was *Ch'ien Men Wai,* "the Outside Town," given over to moneymaking, gambling, brothels, poverty.

Neither the passage of time nor the Communist regime has succeeded in removing all these differences. Certainly, the property-owning classes have lost their privileges and their wall-enclosed mansions are shut, but the character of these districts remains written in the very architecture, despite the new buildings rising in demolished areas. What is more, the senior officials of the regime have taken over the palaces of the royal princes in the Tartar City, while the same poor people live in the same huts of beaten earth beneath the Chinese City's ramparts.

Some suggested excursions are marked on Plan Number 10.

171

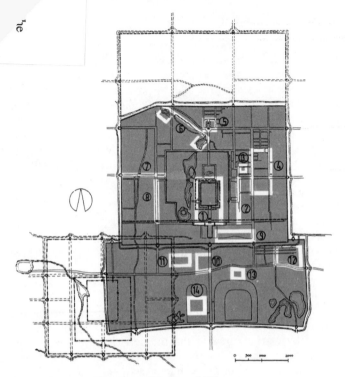

Fourteen Walks of Discovery

FIRST WALK OF DISCOVERY

Districts of the Tartar City

The Imperial City. Thick with palaces and temples, the
Imperial City covered a vast area, stretching beyond the Forbidden City to the east and especially to the north and west.
Its appearance has been profoundly altered by the wide new
avenues recently driven through it, yet much of its original
character remains. At the end of the afternoon it is worth
making a tour around the outside of the Forbidden City, by
Nan Ch'ang Chieh (general map, D5), Pei Ch'ang Chieh
(general map, D4), the Hill of Coal and Pei Chih Tse (general map, E4) and Nan Chih Tse. Take this walk slowly, look
carefully at each suite of courtyards, each half-open gateway.

DISTRICTS AND STREETS

You enter the Imperial City by the first street after T'ien An Men on the west side; it is called Nan Ch'ang Chieh. The porch over the entrance to the street is new: until 1911 the red walls here were still completely closed, and access to this part of the Imperial City was possible only via Pei Hai. The street is long and attractive, lined with trees that in summer are of the brightest green. Immediately on the left was the former *Nan Fu* (Southern Palace) where the Court actors used to live. On either side of Nan Ch'ang Chieh are rows of little low houses, most of them all alike, where once lived the domestic servants of the palace. There are fine vistas to the west over the garden of *Nan Hai*, today strictly closed to tourists: its entrance, at the end of the road leading to *Hsin Hua Men* (western gate of the Forbidden City), is closely guarded. Down from either side of this avenue run rows of narrow *hutung*.

Going toward *Hsin Hua Men*, you cross the moats of the City: the crenellated walls here appear at their highest, and little houses stand close at their feet. Further on, on Ch'ang Chieh, you will see three long-disused temples that are not open to visitors. They are, to the west, the *Lei Shen Miao* (Temple of the God of Thunder), built in 1723, and the *Hsing Lung Sze* (Temple of Prosperity), and to the east the *Fu Yu Sze* (Temple of Blessed Protection), which also dates back to 1723. They seem to be in a good state of preservation and their tiers of roofs rising above the trees are especially fine. (See chapter on Peking temples, pp. 149–168.)

Continuing along the avenue, you come to the end of the Forbidden City and to the Hill of Coal. The beautiful enclosure just to the west of the hill was formerly called the *Ta Kao Hsuan Tien* (Palace of High Heaven). It contains a number of fine pavilions that, alas, cannot be visited, for the palace has been turned into an officers' club. In these pavilions the eunuchs and the female servants of the royal palace were educated, and processions of young virgins were inspected every year on the seventh day of the seventh month by the emperor himself.

After passing between the Hill of Coal and the Northern Ramparts of the City, you go back toward Pei Ch'ang Chieh by *Pei Chih Tse*. Two temples, today administrative offices, lie to the east of the street: the *Feng Shen Miao* (Temple of

173

THE FACE OF PEKING

the God of Truths), then the *Yun Shen Miao* (Temple of the God of Clouds). Pei Chih Tse, with its many modern buildings, is less picturesque than Pei Ch'ang Chieh, but take the first *hutung* to the east after *Tun An Men Ta Chieh*. Here you will lose yourself in a network of narrow alleyways where, at nightfall in summer, everyone seems to be sitting in the cool air on his doorstep. If you look carefully, you may be able to see on your right the high roof of the *Mahakala Miao*, or Mongol Temple (see p. 159).

SECOND WALK OF DISCOVERY

Wan Fu Ching (general map F4 and 5). All foreign visitors know this street of big shops, the Fifth Avenue or Oxford Street of Peking. You should see it at the end of the afternoon when the shops are invaded by Pekingese returning from their work. The *Eastern Market* (general map, F5; see also p. 89) is picturesque, although nowadays rather too clean and organized. Nevertheless you can still drink tea there in a large and famous teahouse, and the market also contains various restaurants. Opposite it is the large *State Store* (Pai Huo Ta Lou), and here too an excursion into the Chinese consumer society is fascinating (see p. 89). And on Saturday afternoons in this street you can see all the families of foreign residents in Peking doing their shopping.

THIRD WALK OF DISCOVERY

District of Tung Sze (general map F5). The Tung Sze is the former name of what is now the *People's Market* (see p. 89). The little street that runs beside it as well as the neighboring alleys are typical of those districts of the Tartar City devoted to commerce and workers' housing. In many ways the Tung Sze resembles the former Bridge of Heaven in the Chinese City: there is the same bustle of crowds around the little stalls selling fruit, cakes, or fritters (the stoves are set up on the very edge of the street in winter), and the same lines of children, though here they are lining up to go into a children's theater. There are also cinemas, big propaganda posters, and big shops, whose façades, however, are less attractive than those in the Chinese City. In sum, the whole area teems with varied and seemingly endless activity.

174

DISTRICTS AND STREETS

FOURTH WALK OF DISCOVERY

The Aristocratic Districts (general map F3). These are not really palaces—the fine dwellings of the princes and nobles were mostly inside the Imperial City—but the once-fashionable suburbs for the bourgeoisie and the intellectuals. These districts consist of all the *hutung* numbered from 1 to 9 stretching to the east of *Ha Ta Men Ta Chieh* (or Chung Wen Men Ta Chieh), between *Chao Yang Men Ta Chieh* and *Chang Tche Sung Lu*.

In this part of the town the rows of Chinese houses are the most harmoniously planned and have the finest proportions. You may not be able to get inside them, but look at least at their gates and roofs. The lintels above the gates are often magnificent, decorated with traditional Chinese subjects (dragons, gods, etc.) or with motifs of Persian or Central Asian inspiration. The roofs are finely proportioned, slightly concave in the center. And the trees, as in all Peking, have a particular charm. Let yourself wander amid the maze of these streets, which are much more complicated to follow than may appear from any map. The stones and bricks are of a luminous gray that you find nowhere else in the capital. This is the Tartar City in all its splendor, and you must see it to get an idea of bourgeois life in Peking fifty to three hundred years ago.

Farther south, in the *Tungtan* district (general map, F4) between *Chao Yang Men* and *Kan Mien hutung*, the houses are a little smaller but have kept their character just as much.

FIFTH WALK OF DISCOVERY

The Towers of the Drum and Bell (general map, E2). These two monuments are at the northern end of the great north-south perspective that cuts right across Peking. The districts around the towers are picturesque but little known.

The Tower of the Drum (Ku Lou) is one of the oldest buildings in Peking. Erected in 1272 by the Mongol emperor Shih Tse, in the midst of the former city of the Yuan, it is an elegant slightly trapezoid building made up of four stories covered with three gray roofs. Every evening at sunset drums were beaten here.

THE FACE OF PEKING

Walk behind this tower, and crowded alleyways will lead you to the *Tower of the Bell,* more interesting than the drum tower although it dates back only to Ch'ien Lung, its earlier buildings having been destroyed. It is made up of two buildings, one on top of the other. On the upper floor is a huge clock, the subject of a touching legend. A humble metal-caster was given the task of making for the emperor the largest bell ever seen. And the poor man didn't succeed because none of his alloys was satisfactory. His daughter saw her father in tears and discovered the reason for his failure: a bell of this size and quality could not be made unless the blood of a virgin was added to the alloy. Without another thought she jumped into the vat of boiling metal, and although her father tried to stop her he couldn't do more than catch hold of one shoe. The resulting bell was the loveliest in the empire and its sound was the most melodious in the world: when struck, it softly murmurs "*hsieh,*" which means "shoe."

Behind the Tower of the Bell you can see the precinct of a former temple and fine tree-shaded houses inhabited by leaders of the regime. The whole district, though less imposing than the nine *hutung* of Ha Ta Men, nevertheless has great character.

SIXTH WALK OF DISCOVERY

The Northern Lakes of the Tartar City (general map, C1 and 2, D2, E2).

Shi Chai Hai (the Lake of the Monasteries), Hsi Hai (the Western Lake), and Hou Hai (the Black Lake) are the most northerly lakes in Peking. They make one of the pleasantest excursions in the city, and here it is a question not of sightseeing but of just wandering around.

Shi Chai Hai is reached by the wide avenue (E2) leading from the Tower of the Drum. Along its northeast bank stretches a group of *hutung* that form a kind of little urban commune devoted essentially to embroidery. The houses lack character, but at least are antique, and the little old shops suggest a sleepy village in the heart of the city.

You should then go back toward Hou Hai. Between the northern bank of this lake and *Ku Lou Hsi Ta Chieh* you will pass in front of a fine temple, the *Kuang Hua Sze* (general map, D2; see chapter on Peking temples, pp. 149–168) before reaching the lake itself. Then just follow the bank. In

176

winter children race over the ice on improvised sleighs; in spring it is always windswept. There are palaces along the banks, and behind the high walls you can make out their low shapes and glazed roofs. All this area gives a great feeling of peace: little old men take their exercise, bent in two over their sticks, and sometimes a group of red-scarved children pass by. At the northern end of Hou Hai is the former palace of Prince Ch'un, while on your way back to the Tower of the Drum via Lou Hsi Ta Chieh you will find on your left the huge gardens and palaces of a residence today occupied by the official representatives of Lamaism in Peking, notably the Panchen Lama. Do not try to get in.

Continuing your tour of the lakes, however, you will get to Hsi Hai. On a little hill on its north bank is a pretty little temple, the *Ching Ye Sze* (general map C1). The *Kao Miao,* or Autumn Temple, which faces it on the opposite bank, has become a factory.

SEVENTH WALK OF DISCOVERY

Fu Cheng Men (*or* Ping Tze Men Ta Chieh; general map, B and C3). This is a broad avenue, lined with picturesque shops and numerous temples, and usually crowded. In the neighboring *hutung*, where the roadways are piled high with vegetables or coal, you can wander about happily without getting lost. Here a whole teeming population has taken over the former middle-class mansions as well as such temples as the White Pagoda. Note the chemists' shops (drugstores) of Peking: side by side on the same pavement of Fu Cheng Men Ta Chieh is a large European drugstore and a traditional little dispensary, both clearly run by the same people. Each trusts in his own gods. . . .

EIGHTH WALK OF DISCOVERY

Hsi Tan (general map C4 and 5). This wide avenue, its southern end at the Gate of Death, corresponds on the west to Wan Fu Ching in the east. Like Wan Fu Ching, it is lined with numerous shops and has an important covered market: the *Hsitan Bazaar*, rather more crowded with Chinese, and with fewer tourists, than Wan Fu Ching. You should go there on a Saturday or Sunday afternoon—the street itself and the shops are of little interest, but look at the crowds, almost as thick as in the great Ch'ien Men Avenue.

The *hutung* on its west side are, by contrast, rather quiet and they enclose some fine houses. Stroll around the area on foot and you will come across gateways opening onto shady courts, and you will be followed by groups of giggling children.

NINTH WALK OF DISCOVERY

The Legation District (general map, E and F5). At first

sight you would think yourself in the streets of some small European town: the houses are mostly red brick, in the middle of vast walled precincts, the "compounds" of the former legations. For the older Europeans of Peking this area has plenty of nostalgic memories. The French Embassy used to occupy the corner of Tung Chia Min Hsiang (former Street of the Legations) and Tai Chih Chang (former Marco Polo Street): the huge red gateway is still guarded by stone lions, as well as by two flesh-and-blood soldiers, for today it is used by the Chinese government to house its more illustrious visitors. Opposite, on the Street of the Legations, was the German Embassy, and farther on, the British Embassy and the large barracks-like American Embassy. There was a post office (indeed, it still exists as such) kept by the mother of René Lys, hero of Victor Segalen's novel, while the Bank of China today occupies the premises of the former Bank of Indochina. The first *hutung* on the right as you go up the former Marco Polo Street from the Street of the Legations is called Tai Chang San Tiao, and here were the barracks of the French garrison, as well as the center where Teilhard de Chardin lived for so long. Just in front—and before you get to the cultural section of the present French Embassy—was the famous French grocery, "Père Nicolas."

Needless to say, the district today is rather deserted: only a few embassies are still installed, and they not for long.

TENTH WALK OF DISCOVERY

Districts of the Chinese City

Pa Ta Hutung ("the Eight Large Hutung"; general map, D and E6). Just behind the Ch'ien Men gate are the remnants of what before the Second World War was the "smart" shopping district of Peking, and the main area for good restaurants, nightclubs, gambling clubs, and other entertainments—a sort of Times Square, Soho, or Montmartre all mixed up with a sleazy version of Fifth Avenue, Bond Street, or the Rue de la Paix. Cheek by jowl with the smartest establishments were brothels and secret opium dens that made this area, *Ch'ien Men Wai*, the center of Peking night life. Here people played cards, dice, dominos, mah-jongg. But all these "blemishes of capitalism" have been swept away by modern China's austere puritanism.

It is still worth visiting this district, for the manner in which the new regime has eradicated the traces of past corruption is rather fascinating. The former big luxury shops, with their huge display windows and their front courts protected by iron grilles, have become State stores where blue cotton is sold by the yard. The gambling and other dens have also been "purified" and turned to more edifying uses. Their colonnaded façades and grand staircases now house youth clubs or new shops. As for the infamous haunts in the two little streets parallel to Ch'ien Men Ta Chieh, they have been made into a whole series of teahouses and booths selling fritters. The Sunday crowds come to enjoy themselves here, for the area still contains Peking's luxury shops, selling silks and fur coats and hats.

To get to know this unusual part of Peking, you should leave the Tartar City and walk down Ch'ien Men Ta Chieh until you come to Ta Sha La on your right. It is easy to recognize for its entrance is a big red arch covered with Chinese lettering. Ta Sha La and the streets parallel to it, all full of shops and other businesses, are worth exploring. Then cut back through the little, rather poorer streets that cross it. Take a look at *Lang Fang Erh Chiao*, a bit to the north, the old "Jewelers' street."

As you return to Ch'ien Men along Ch'ien Men Ta Chieh you pass the former luxury stores whose façades are decorated with wood paneling, ceramic tiles, and stone lions and dragons. Today most of these shops sell foodstuffs—all sorts of rice, tea, and flour—but some still look quite imposing.

ELEVENTH WALK OF DISCOVERY

Liu Li Chang (general map D6). This is another part of the town well known to tourists, but they visit only the area of the antique shops, ignoring the little neighboring alleys. And that is a pity, for Liu Li Chang too knew its moment of glory. The area owes its name to a factory, today vanished, which made glazed tiles. And the celebrated temple beside Nan Hsin Hua Chueh has also disappeared, its enclosure now occupied by offices. A fair used to be held there, and all the bargain-hunters of Peking would come and rummage among the emperor's cast-offs.

Following Liu Li Chang eastward, you cross an area full of shops—rather like Ta Sha La save that it is for the working people of Peking rather than for the richer Chinese or for-eigners. Here the old shops are very picturesque: there are street-stalls as in medieval Europe, dimly lit little places with narrow windows where artisans of all sorts are at work. There are restaurants and cookshops, as well as tailor, saddlers, and strange open-air butchers. Though many of the streets give the impression of being culs-de-sac, don't turn back, for in fact Peking has few culs-de-sac and the alleys usually end in an abrupt bend that leads into another *hutung*. Note, too, the simple carved pediments of the more sophisticated shops. Here and there you will come across reminders of some now dis-used local temple, such as the one in the extension of the street that finally becomes Ta Sha La: the *Kuan Yin Sze*, a temple dedicated to Kuan Yin, goddess of mercy.

Continuing eastward, you will get back into Ch'ien Men Ta Chieh.

TWELFTH WALK OF DISCOVERY

Northeast corner of the Chinese City (general map, G and H6). This is a particularly derelict part of Peking. Alongside the actual *hutung* are rows of wooden shacks, each lived in by whole families. The city's housing authorities are aware of the problems caused by such slums in the heart of the city—but China has so many other problems too.

Walk down the narrow gray alleys of this area and stroll beside the moats of the Tartar City. People will be washing their linen, and children paddling in the water. Right in the corner of the City, in front of a temple-turned-factory (the *Pan Tao Kung*), is the oldest bridge in Peking. It goes back to the first days of the Mongol dynasty and bears curious in-scriptions. But do not try to take too many photos of this area:

the Chinese are proud and do not like their poverty being spied on.

THIRTEENTH WALK OF DISCOVERY

Lake of the Golden Fish (Chin Yu Chih; general map, E7). Another poor quarter of Peking, it formerly contained several pools and ponds with temples standing on their banks. Now the pools have been joined together to form a kind of lake, and you can walk around it and watch the children fishing. It is oddly situated below the level of the main streets, between small low houses joined one to the other. The temples have now disappeared, save for the *Ching Chung Miao* ("Temple of the Knight Loyal unto Death) to the northeast of the lake, which of course is not in use. Like the Pan Tao Kung district, this area is typical of a whole section of the Chinese City rarely visited by foreigners.

FOURTEENTH WALK OF DISCOVERY

Tien Chiao (the "Bridge of Heaven"; general map, D and E7). Once this was one of the best-known districts of Peking, but by the 1960s it had lost most of its former rather special character. As for the "Bridge of Heaven," it is no use looking for it: it never existed. "Heaven" may indicate that this was a paradise of hoodlums, pickpockets, and low-class prostitutes. The whole area was a maze of smelly little streets, wretched brothels, and places where such typically Pekingese entertainers as jugglers and puppet showmen used to gather. Paul Tillard, the French novelist, gives a fine description of the onetime atmosphere of the area in *Le Montreur des Marionettes.*

Today it has all been drained, cleaned, pulled down, and rebuilt by the Communist regime. Until 1966 there were still some amusing entertainments here, and on weekends in addition to the jugglers and puppet shows you could see wrestlers, acrobats, shadow-theater actors, and a fascinating storyteller. There were open-air restaurants, small shops, and lots of cinemas showing propaganda films. But the Cultural Revolution seems to have swept away the last traces of what was one of the liveliest corners of Peking. Will the acrobats, conjurors, and others reappear one day? It is hard to believe so.

THE SURROUNDINGS OF PEKING

After the "Liberation"—as it is called in People's China—
the surroundings of Peking made up a vast vaguely defined
area, stretching as far north as Jehol and Kalgan, and as far
west as the Yung Kang caves near Ta-tung. The area contained a number of temples, archaeological sites, and several
groups of tombs.

One day the security services of the new regime took a

map and a compass, placed the point of the compass in the center of Peking, and drew a circle thirty miles in diameter. This now defines the "surroundings of Peking." A narrow corridor allows you to escape to the northwest to visit the Ming Tombs and the Great Wall, and another corridor leads to the airport. But for a foreigner it is absolutely impossible to go beyond these closely guarded limits.

That is to say, not only have Ta Tung and the fortified town of Jehol been closed to foreigners since 1949, but a large part of the Western Hills—despite their proximity and their fabulous temples—has also been out of bounds, as well as the tombs of the west and east in their splendid setting beside the Great Wall. Map Number 11—rather sketchy, for modern maps do not exist and the old ones are out of date—shows the whereabouts of the main monuments to the west and northwest of Peking. The Ming Tombs and the Great Wall are respectively thirty and forty-five miles farther north.

The Summer Palaces

To escape the rigors of the Peking summer (104°F, or 40°C, in the shade, with high humidity in July and August), the Manchu kings used to seek refuge in residences that were cooler and less austere than the "Winter Palaces" of the Forbidden City.

There were several of these "Summer Palaces." The Manchu built two groups of them northwest of Peking: the *Yuan Ming Yuan*, or "Garden of Prudence and Clarity," and the *Wan Shou Shan,* or "Mountain of Ten Thousand Years of Longevity." But if you simply mention "Summer Palace" when you get to Peking, it is to Wan Shou Shan that you will be taken, for the Peking tourist authorities regard it as one of the city's treasures. Frankly, its prodigious array of "chinoiseries"—pavilions and lakes, temples and galleries—are a little too sparkling and freshly tarted-up to be really interesting: the lake and the country around are charming, but the palaces themselves are not.

As for Yuan Ming Yuan, no one will mention it, save perhaps to remind you politely that it was destroyed by British and French troops in 1860. The lake of the Summer Palace is for today's Chinese "a picture from old history books."

THE FACE OF PEKING

The former Summer Palace: Yuan Ming Yuan

It was K'ang Hsi, the grandfather of Ch'ien Lung who built the first palaces of Yuan Ming Yuan and in 1710 presented to his son Yung Cheng. Ch'ien Lung enlarged and decorated them, and turned them into legendary castles that Western visitors described with wonder. Then in 1860 British and French troops occupied the palaces and a British general decided to destroy them all by way of reprisal. The damage was great but not irreparable: some of the buildings were not harmed at all and Tzu Hsi was later able to repair others, though she also built a new residence—and the original Yuan Ming Yuan, first sullied by the "diabolical foreigners" and then left in neglect, was finally overgrown by weeds and thickets.

Its few remaining ruins are nevertheless fascinating: these pillars, these fragments of palaces, and these fountains rising above the rice paddies are the purest European baroque! The Manchu kings called in Jesuits to build their homes; as a result, several square miles in the neighborhood of Peking were covered with some two hundred palaces, pavilions, and terraces of European inspiration, as well as a network of canals and streams, punctuated by extraordinary fountains topped with baroque ornaments and statues.

Not much is left: a number of capitals of pillars half buried in the earth, a group of pseudo-Doric columns, a huge fountain with a shell-shaped stone basin that still seems to be pouring its water into a marshy pool, a bizarre gateway finely decorated with arabesques and ornamental rockeries. All around are walls with gaping holes and tottering masonry.

It is hard to find Yuan Ming Yuan, for the landscape has swallowed it up and the official Chinese guides do not include it in their organized excursions. All you need do, however (see Plan Number 11), is leave Peking in the direction of Wan Shou Shan and turn right after Peking University, down the road leading to the technical university, until you come to the first turning to the left. About half a mile and two curves down this road, an unpaved road leads to the edge of the first ruins. The excursion is worth it, for all around these ruins stretches a typical Chinese landscape of rice paddies, cornfields, villages, and hamlets. If you go to see this Jesuit-built palace, you will also see the real China.

THE SURROUNDINGS OF PEKING

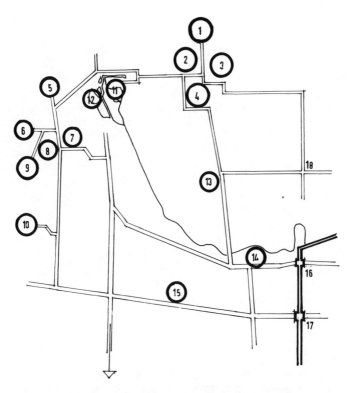

The Summer Palace and the Western Hills

1. The Sports Institute
2. Ruins of the Former
   Summer Palace
3. Univ. of Technology
4. University of Peking
5. Ta Fo Sze
6. Pi Yun Sze
7. The Circular Fortress
8. The Tibetan Towers
9. The Game Park
10. Pa Ta Shu
11. The Summer Palace
12. The Jade Fountain
13. Hotel of Friendship
14. Zoo
15. Pa Li Chang
16. Hsi Chih Men
17. Fu Cheng Men
18. Ten Sheng Men

THE FACE OF PEKING

The New Summer Palace: Wan Shou Shan

Wan Shou Shan is generally regarded as the creation of Tzu Hsi, though this isn't quite true. In fact Ch'ien Lung built a palace on this spot soon after 1751, "the Mountain of the Ten Thousand Years of Longevity," which he planned for the dowager empress Nihulu. So much did she love the Hangchow region that she dreamed of re-creating its landscape of lakes, islands, and trees near Peking, and her son did it for her. But after her death the palace fell in ruins, and after 1893 Tzu Hsi rebuilt it entirely, considerably enlarging it in the process. To do so, she used up most of her personal fortune and then took large sums from China's military and naval budgets. And it is her memory that is today enshrined at Wan Shou Shan—this "Palace of Happy Old Age" that she built to protect herself against death.

The palace is worth visiting, for the countryside is lovely, but there is no need to spend too much time on it. It rises beside a triangular lake fed by the streams from the Jade Fountain that you can see on the western horizon. There are two aspects to a visit to Wan Shou Shan: the palaces on the north side and the tour of the lake.

The Palaces of Tzu Hsi

Plan Number 12 shows the site of the main buildings, numbered as follows:

(1) The entrance—a modern, flamboyant gateway.

(2) The "Palace of Old Age and of the Reward of Goodness" (Jen Shou Tien), where Tzu Hsi held public audiences.

(3) The "Palace of the Cascades of White Jade" (Yu Lang Tang), where Tzu Hsi kept Kuang Hsu locked up (see pp. 24–25) after she herself had left the Winter Palaces.

(4) The "Garden of Pleasant Harmony" (Te Ho Yuan): an interesting group of pavilions forming a theatrical stage several floors high (to store the scenery) and a hall for the public.

(5) The "Hall of Happy Old Age" (Lo Shou Tang) was Tzu Hsi's private residence.

(6) The "Pavilion of the Favorable Clouds" (Yang Yun Hsuan) was the residence of her ladies-in-waiting.

(7) A covered gallery that runs the length of all the

palaces beside the edge of the lake. It is decorated with paintings and is one of the major attractions of Wan Shou Shan. But not everyone agrees on its merits.

(8) A complicated pai-lou at the entrance of the road to the temples.

(9) The "Palace of the Jagged Clouds" (Pai Yun Tien): This is on the site of the temple built by Ch'ien Lung on the sixtieth anniversary of the death of his mother and destroyed by the "imperialists" in 1860. At this point you begin climbing the "Mountain of Longevity."

(10) The "Pavilion of Bronze" (Pao Yun Ko) dates back to 1755.

(11) The "Temple of the Ten Thousand Buddhas" (or "Temple of the Clouds"—(Fo Hsiang Ko): Its high tower dominates the surrounding landscape, which is exactly that of a traditional Chinese painting—the lake, pavilions, and hump-backed bridges must be seen from here if you are to catch their full charm.

(12) The "Tower of Tibetan Prayer" (Chuan Lu Tsang).

(13) The "Sea of Perfect Wisdom" (Chih Huei Hai): One of the few really interesting buildings in Wan Shou Shan, with a fine pai-lou in front of it, it is built entirely of glazed bricks and ceramics and stands above the northern slopes of the hill. Beyond it there used to be some palaces and pavilions, which are now in ruins. On the west part of the mountain are various temples and pavilions.

(14) The "Promenade Past Beautiful Landscapes" (Hsu Chung Yu).

(15) The "Boat of Marble" (Ching Yen Fang, which means "the stream and the boats on the tranquil sea"). This is the famous pavilion of marble and carved wood built by Tzu Hsi. It is not very beautiful.

(16) The "Tower of the Pure and Everlasting View" (Yen Ching Shang Lou).

(17) The "Temple of the Gathered Clouds" (Yun Huei Sze).

On your way down the east side of the mountain, you come across the most attractive buildings of Wan Shou Shan:

(18) The "Temple of the Manifestation of Divinity" (Shan Hsien Sze).

(19) The "Belvedere of Flowers" (Hua Chang Ko).

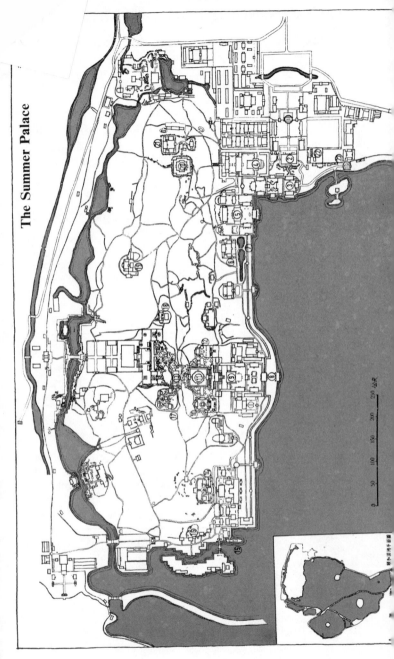

The Summer Palace

188

THE SURROUNDINGS OF PEKING

(20) The "Belvedere of Great Happiness" (Ching Fu Ko): The aged dowager empress used to walk up here on nights when the moon was full.

(21) The "Gardens of Harmony in Pleasure" (Hsieh Ch'ou Yuan): A group of pavilions dating back to the days of Ch'ien Lung's festivities.

A tour around the lake

It takes more than two hours to walk round Wan Shou Shan's lake—but it is a very pleasant walk, in spring and in autumn, especially in the first days of October when every conceivable shade of red seems to flourish on the shores.

Starting from the east bank, you pass in turn:

(22) The tomb of Yen Lu Chu Tsai: this was built by Tzu Hsi to the memory of a former governor of Peking, an astrologist who had also been honored by Genghis Khan.

(23) The "Tower of the God of Literature" (Wen Chang Ko).

Then come:

Ch'ien Lung's famous bronze bullock, set up to guard the lake.

The fine bridge with seventeen arches that leads to the island of Wung Wan Tao and to the Temple of the Imperial Dragon. South of the island is a big public swimming pool open all the summer.

The island of Feng Huang Tung, or the rock of the Phoenix, where the ladies of the Court once used to go to give birth.

The west side of the lake has fewer buildings but is quieter and perhaps more beautiful. The lake is divided in two here by a long dike broken at intervals by beautiful humpbacked bridges: the best known of them is the "Bridge of the Girdle of Jade" at the western end.

Besides its historical and cultural interest, the Summer Palace offers the tourist a sight of typical Chinese crowds, who throng here all through the week to stroll around and take the country air. You see them everywhere—up the steep pathways, beside the lake, even in the lake when the weather is warm.

Pioneers and Red Guards pass by at a steady pace or play war games in the avenues, people eat ices and fritters and go canoeing on the lake. When Chairman Mao gives the word, out they go in their thousands every day to learn to swim, the young and the not so young, splashing around in a somewhat muddy water that dully reflects the façades of the palaces. Young art students, alone in a quiet corner of the park, clutch their crayons and concentrate on sketching the delicate lace-work of a marble bridge on huge sheets of white paper. These sights alone repay a visit to the Summer Palace.

The Western Hills

The area generally known as the Western Hills, closed since the Cultural Revolution, is due to be reopened soon. It offers possibilities for excursions and discoveries that are unrivaled in the immediate vicinity of Peking. It is also, along with the Great Wall and the Ming Tombs, the only excursion zone normally open to tourists and foreign residents. The old classical guidebooks deal too summarily with some of the temples and palaces here, and go into great detail about others. All are worth looking at, however, for here more than anywhere one can still summon up an image of the old traditional China of parks, pleasure haunts, and lonely temples.

Not that they are mere "hills"—rather, a succession of little mountains with rounded summits, each two to three thousand feet high, outlined against the horizon. They are bluish in the distance, violet-colored on fine summer evenings, and russet in autumn. Around them there is always a kind of mist that blurs their outlines and shrouds the valleys below. The air here is fresher than on the plain, and when the heat of Peking becomes overpowering, the woods and streams of the Western Hills offer a delicious freshness.

A visit should not be too rapid. The dogged tourist who "does" the Western Hills in the morning and the Summer Palace in the afternoon will bring back merely the souvenir of three temples, neither more nor less beautiful or interesting than those he has seen elsewhere. Moreover, you don't go to the Western Hills to visit temples: you go there for a walk, and the temples are incidental. This nuance is important and very Chinese. The temples in these hills—some of which, such as the Sanctuary of the Reclining Buddha, date back to the eighth century—are not museums or showplaces. Five centuries ago they were centers of prayer and meditation, and they remain havens of peace, gardens of reverie. Our European grandparents, colonialists in morning dress, used to "hire a temple for the season" in these hills. They moved out of the Legation District with their servants and luggage to spend the summer there—like the dowager empress in her Summer Palace a few years earlier. Evidence of this bygone age—numerous villas, luxurious mansions, or little pavilions—still perch on the sides of the hills, at Pa Ta Shu or in the Hunting Park.

Your official tourist guide will tell you that these delightful resorts are today "the property of the Chinese people." He speaks no more than the truth. You have only to take a Sunday walk in the gardens of the hunting park to see China's youth everywhere, wearing shorts and open shirts in summer and warm blue coats in winter. Some look carefree, some subdued. Solemnly the loving couples climb hand in hand up the steps leading to the porcelain pagoda; they seem to want to turn their private happiness into the serious matter that (the Chinese propaganda press tells us) it should be, involving not only the individual heart but the whole of society.

Children with red scarves and red streamers and banners troop by to the rhythm of a drum. But there are other kids rushing along the pathways, and teen-agers in groups of three or four having a gay old time on the steep slopes. And there are also the lonely ones: dreamers walking about with books in their hands or lingering on a belvedere to gaze toward the plain of Peking that lies in the distance beyond the agglomeration of rocks and pines below. On the horizon they can see the pagoda of the Jade Fountain.

The main monuments of the Western Hills were not all open to the public even before the Cultural Revolution. For instance, the famous "Jade Fountain," a group of buildings that includes numerous pavilions, fine sculptures, and above all a tall pagoda visible from far off, has become a sort of military camp. On the other hand, it is usually possible to see the Temples of the Reclining Buddha and of the Blue Clouds, as well as the Hunting Park, Ch'ien Lung's circular fortress, Pa Ta Shu (the eight hallowed spots of the mountain), and, on the way back, the pagoda of Pa Li Chang.

The Temple of the Reclining Buddha (Ta Fo Tze)

This is probably the oldest temple in the area, dating back to the eighth century. Needless to say, very little remains of it from that period. It is a succession of courtyards and palaces,

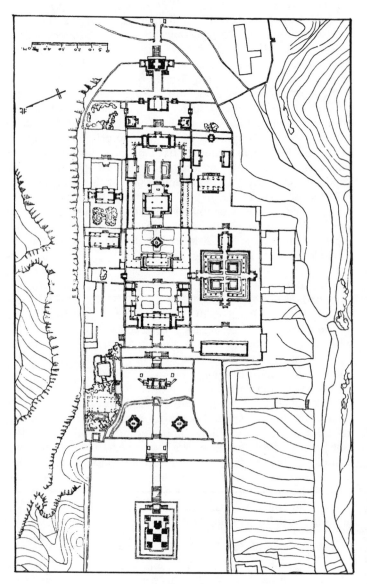

The Temple of the Blue Clouds

tastefully and discreetly redecorated, and shaded by trees centuries old. The buildings are large and numerous and you approach them down a long avenue of cypresses. There is nothing much to see, however, except for the huge Reclining Buddha in one of the palaces. It is a vast statue, drowsy and smiling—a bronze Mongol effigy that replaced an earlier wooden statue. The Buddha is entirely cloaked in a long gilded robe and only his feet are bare. In homage, pilgrims in olden days used to leave their shoes in front of the statue. This image of the Reclining Buddha, awaiting his divine awakening, has a classic place in Buddhist mythology, and in Peking alone there used to be several temples dedicated to him.

The Temple of the Blue Clouds (Pi Yun Sze)

This is the most famous temple in the Western Hills. Foreign residents in Peking used to know it well and went there in droves in the 1930s for picnics or outdoor parties. A certain Nachbaur, an Alsatian émigré to farthest China who ran a publishing house and published a humorous monthly paper called *Yellow Laughter*, even went so far as to found an "Order of the Green Cloud." Its members, who included some of the leading foreign residents in Peking, used to meet regularly in a small hall of the temple, and to belong to this brotherhood was an honor much sought after.

The temple evokes other, more serious memories, too—including that of Yun Ching, an immensely rich eunuch who played a role rather like that of Fouquet under Louis XIV. He built himself a sumptuous residence and a mausoleum in the shadow of the temple, and then, accused of dishonesty, ended his days in prison.

Pi Yun Sze is made up of a suite of buidings faced with glazed tiles, rising gently one above the other to a fine marble stupa, set at the end of a valley between the hills. To the left of the main temples is a curious hall, plunged in semidarkness, where the statues of five hundred *lohan*, or saints of Buddhist mythology, keep vigil. Seated and life-sized, they offer an astonishing spectacle: made of gilded and lacquered wood, they are all grimacing or smiling, sometimes behind the most fearsome beards. It is the tradition to burst into guffaws of laughter at these figures, although many of them are really rather beautiful.

Before you reach this hall, you come first to a fine marble pai-lou; then a gateway guarded by statues of four furious-looking kings, made of plaster or stucco, each some ten feet tall; then a temple dedicated to the "Buddha Yet To Come," a huge statue, smiling and pot-bellied. And the last hall in the temple contains the glass coffin that the Soviet Union presented to China after the death of Sun Yat-sen. The gift arrived too late, for Sun Yat-sen was already buried, but the empty coffin, together with a hat and a walking-stick and a little collection of photographs, are there as a reminder of the militant career of the great Chinese democrat. His body was later transported to Nanking.

By an inner stairway you can climb to the platform of the marble stupa crowned with six small towers and decorated with Indian-style sculptures representing scenes from Buddhist mythology. It offers a fine panorama over the complete layout of the lower halls of the temple and over the plain beyond. In fact, this is the best general view you can get of the Peking plain from the Western Hills, fuller than the view from Pa Ta Shu.

The Hunting Park of the Scented Mountain (Hsiang Shan)

The extraordinary thing about this mountain is that, thanks to its flowers and trees, it *is* scented, from early spring until the end of autumn. Its trees are the most beautiful in the Western Hills.

In the old days there were a number of royal hunting parks around Peking, but they have given way to housing developments (in the south) or else are outside the limits allowed to foreigners (to the northwest). The Scented Mountain, which was used by all the emperors from the days of the Liao onward, is the only one of these parks you can visit today. Of the temples and pagodas that it once contained, not much remains, for the most interesting of them fell into ruins under the Ming or were destroyed more recently after a good deal of plundering. On the other hand, senior officials of the Kuomintang built within the park a number of modern villas with terraces and balustrades in mock-Marienbad style, and because of the beauty of the site some of the temples have been rebuilt. But little is left of the original monuments save a few steles and a pretty "porcelain pagoda" (actually covered with glazed tiles) that stands elegantly in the east part of the garden.

This book will not attempt to guide you through the labyrinthine pathways of the mountain: when I tried to follow the official maps posted at the entries, I simply got lost. You may be luckier and may even find the tomb of the last Liao. At any rate, you will find the park's pleasant restaurant, which is just at the rear of a true Chinese inn made up of courtyards and enclosures. Here you can have lunch or dinner and even pass the night if you warn them in advance—and above all drink a cup of tea when the weather is hot.

The road from the Hunting Park to Pa Ta Shu

Between Hsiang Chang and Pa Ta Shu the road follows the foot of the hills for some six miles. On either side there is great activity: peasants at work, pushing or dragging their handcarts and mules, or khaki-clad soldiers marching up and down, some holding rifles. Much of the former charm of this road has vanished amid smoke from the new little factories or white dust from the big building sites along the foot of the hills. Nevertheless, to the right, between the new buildings and the farms, you can still see traces of the past: Tibetan-style towers rise up from the lower slopes of the hills; they date from the mid-eighteenth century and were built either to commemorate victories or battles, or to give battle practice to Chinese soldiers who were thus trained in the assault of the type of fortresses their enemies used.

This part of the hills has always been a military zone: everywhere there are barracks and camps. Even so, one's attention is drawn to a glazed roof, yellow and green, that crowns a tall building lost amid the foliage, the remains of some temple. But there are two soldiers on guard to stop you from getting in, and the same applies to other enclosures in the area.

The Circular Fortress

Beside the plain, to the east of the road to Pa Ta Shu and about two miles from the entrance to the Park of the Scented Mountain, is the "Circular Fortress" or "Circular Terrace" built by Ch'ien Lung. It is one of the most picturesque spots in the Peking area. Built in 1749, it is a circular enclosure dominated by two elegant pavilions with painted and carved woodwork, and it has never had more than symbolic value. It commemorated a victory of General Fu Hung and the Imperial Army over the Tibetan forces. Later, the emperor used it as an observation post when he wanted to watch his troops on maneuvers or at archery practice in the plain.

The monument as a whole is made up, first, of a heavy stone bridge close to the road; then, fifty yards beyond, there is an attractive pavilion with a veranda whose woodwork, although not in good repair, has kept its delicacy and rich multicolored decoration. Just behind this pavilion is the fortress itself, nearly two hundred feet in diameter. You enter it by a gate that today is bare and without decoration only to find that there isn't really anything inside the walls. The two pavilions stand above a circular road, and two steep ramps lead up to it.

But this banal description gives little idea of the charm of this forlorn construction. A people's commune has today set up its workshop and warehouses here, and whereas in most such cases this destroys a historic building, here the peasants who live in the citadel have found its amenities adequate and thus have not disfigured them. Horses graze in front of the main entrance, the veranda of the main pavilion is full of tools, and although its finely carved gates have suffered from the passage of time, at least they are intact, including their transparent paper paneling. Behind them you can sense a life going on, people's homes. . . .

Pa Ta Shu

The walk to Pa Ta Shu is long and tiring: you have to climb up a steep path into the foothills, then drop down into a little valley, then climb again up the bed of a rocky stream—take sturdy shoes!

But it is also a pleasant walk. Eight temples are scattered along the two slopes of a valley that opens onto the plain of Peking. They are neither especially large nor beautiful, but most are quite old, and their charm comes from their isolation and—why not?—from their very decrepitude. The walls are still standing but mostly covered with brambles, trees have grown up in the terracelike courtyards that overlook the country below, and the dark halls of the temples are full of tottering statues of *lohan* or *Kuan Yin* in gilded wood.

These, in the order in which you will reach them, are the eight holy spots of Pa Ta Shu:

Ch'ang An Sze, or the "Temple of Eternal Peace," is slightly apart from the others, to the left of the paved path that leads to Pa Ta Shu. It offers little interest, for it has recently been entirely rebuilt.

Lin Kuang Sze, or "Temple of the Tooth of Buddha," dates back to the Sung but was largely rebuilt in 1478. The Indian occupation armies burned down its large pagoda in 1900, and this has only recently been rebuilt by the Chinese Buddhist Society, in order to house a relic of Buddha. The pagoda isn't exactly beautiful—a tall modern tower painted flaming red— nor are the rather too tidy buildings that surround it. The only building to keep a certain air of mystery is the little tea-house at the rear of the enclosure, beside a lake of dark water.

All the temples you come to next have remained largely in their original state. To reach them, you simply follow the footpath along the right side of the large pagoda.

San Shan An, or "Monastery of the Three Mountains," is a small temple overgrown with trees and flowers. It was built first in 1442, then rebuilt by Wan Li and Ch'ien Lung.

Ta Pei Sze, or "Temple of Great Mercy," another Sung temple rebuilt by K'ang Hsi, is large and includes some fine statues. Its architecture is typical of the older temples outside the city walls: halls often at a distance from each other, buildings on steep slopes, terraces, and so on.

Lung Wang T'ang, or "Temple of the Dragon's Spring," owes its name to the spring that fills a little pool in the first enclosure. Originally a temple of the Liao dynasty, it was rebuilt several times till the days of Yung Lo, who gave it its present name. It is also on a steep slope, and makes up a fine ensemble of halls and terraces with views over the plain.

THE FACE OF PEKING

Hsiang Chieh Sze, or "Temple of the Scented World," is a former royal residence, where the emperor used to stay during his visits to Pa Ta Shu. Its origins are uncertain, but it seems that Yung Lo built it on the ruins of a T'ang sanctuary. It is the most important of the eight holy spots of Pa Ta Shu—and many of its halls are still in use, as a school or as dwellings.

Pao Chu Tung, or "Cavern of the Precious Stones," is situated high up beyond Hsiang Chieh Sze. It was founded near a grotto by a monk named Lu Shih; two small boys helped him to build the sanctuary and then, according to legend, were turned into benevolent dragons. The view from here is as fine and extensive as from Hsiang Chieh Sze, but not everyone has the courage to climb so high.

Pi Mo Yen, or "Gate of the Mysterious Spirit," is on the other side of the valley of Pa Ta Shu—so to reach it you must go down to Hsiang Chieh Sze, then take the road along the bottom of the valley. Pi Mo Yen is relatively recent, dating back only to the Ming period, and includes a legendary stone to which it owes its name.

Pa Li Chang: Some three miles from Ping Tze Men, this is a pagoda fourteen stories high, the only relic of a temple dedicated to Kuan Yin and destroyed by needy monks who sold its timber by the hundredweight. Today it stands in a picturesque and lively village.

The Ming Tombs

This is the finest excursion you can make in the Peking region. Unfortunately, the travel agencies with their tight schedules think fit to herd their flocks of tourists to the Great Wall and to these royal tombs in one day, whereas you need to spend at least a whole day there to admire them and appreciate their charm. My advice is to leave early in the morning, picnic somewhere amid the ruins of an abandoned tomb, and wait to see the sun set over the valley.

The emperors of China built these tombs on the same scale as their Empire: gigantic. They are grouped in a special spot, carefully chosen for precise reasons, topographical and geomantic: the last long sleep of each emperor needed to benefit from the airs of the most propitious spirits. So there are three groups of tombs in the Peking region: the "Western Tombs" (Hsi Ling), the "Eastern Tombs" (Tung Ling), which were built by the Manchu and are closed to visitors, and the "Thirteen Tombs" (Shi San Ling) of the Ming. The first Ming emperor, Hung Wu, reigned at Nanking and his tomb is still there; but after the death of his son it was Yung Lo, the true founder of Peking, who chose the site of what was to become Shi San Ling and was himself buried there in 1424. And all the other kings of that dynasty (except Ching Tai, an involuntary usurper who is buried at the Jade Fountain) were later laid to rest at his side. Each emperor had a name while he lived and another when he died, and each tomb had a name of its own. The thirteen Ming sepulchres are listed on page 200.

The first historic building on your way from Peking is a pai-lou (18) in white marble, finely sculpted and dating from the time of Chia Ching (1540). It marks the beginning of the triumphal way leading to the tomb of Yung Lo. Next you come across the Great Red Gate (Ta Hung Men) (17), a vast construction 120 feet high, then the Pavilion of the Stele (Pei Ting) (16), which houses the largest stele in all China: it is twenty-eight feet high and stands on the fourteen-foot statue of a turtle made from a single piece of white marble. It was erected in 1425 by Tien Shun to the memory of Yung Lo.

Then comes the extraordinary "Alley of the Animals," (15), consisting of twelve pairs of marble animals on either side of the road, alternately crouching and standing up, followed by four pairs of warriors and ministers, all guarding the emperors' eternal sleep. Each statue is a masterpiece of enigmatic symbolism.

The site of the Ming Tombs was apparently chosen with great consideration of religious dogma. A semi-circular range of hills to the north acted as a barrier to the evil winds of the northern steppes, while a stream bounded the tombs on the south.

Today, as you journey toward the Ming Tombs, you will pass Tiger Mountain (19) and a low mountainous range called the Jaggon Mountains (20).

You will also pass the Ming Reservoir, (21) which was constructed at the beginning of the Great Leap Forward in 1956, and drained much of the water from the river flowing through

NUMBER OF TOMB ON MAP 13	DATE OF REIGN	NAME OF TOMB	EMPEROR'S NAME AS RULER	EMPEROR'S POSTHUMOUS NAME
1	1403–24	Chang Ling	Yung Lo	Chang Tsu
2	1425	Hsien Ling	Hung Hsi	Jen Tsung
3	1426–35	Ching Ling	Hsuan Teh	Hsuan Tsung
4	1436–49 1457–64*	Yu Ling Tien Shun	Cheng Tung	Ying Tsung
5	1465–75	Mou Ling	Cheng Hua	Hsien Tsung
6	1488–1505	Tai Lung	Hung Chih	Hsia Tsung
7	1506–21	Kang Ling	Cheng Teh	Wu Tsung
8	1522–66	Yung Ling	Chia Ching	Shih Tsung
9	1567–72	Chao Lung	Lung Ching	Mu Tsung
10	1573–1619	Ting Ling	Wan Li	Shegg Tsung
11	1620	Ching Ling	Tai Chang	Kuang Tsung
12	1621–27	Teh Ling	Tien Chi	Hsi Tsung
13	1628–43	Sze Ling	Chung Cheng	Yi Tsung

* Cheng Tung, after an eight-year interregnum, returned to power under the name of Tien Shun.

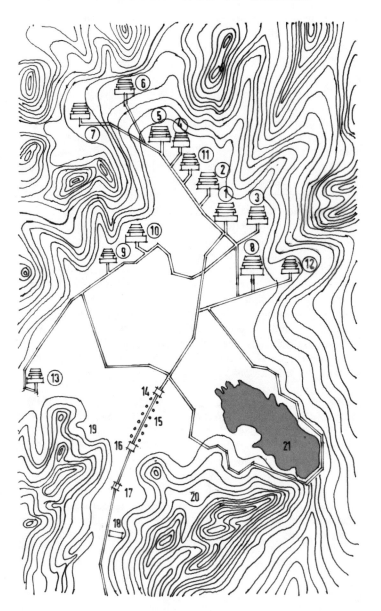

The Ming Tombs

the necropolis. A good portion of the six-square-mile valley is now farmed by the Thirteen Tombs People's Commune.

After another gateway, (14), the "Gate of the Road of the Star," you arrive finally at the tomb of Yung Lo. A complete visit to the valley should include the tomb of the third Ming, a few abandoned tombs in the neighborhood, and the open tomb of Wan Li (10. Ting Ling). All the tombs were built on the same model as Yung Lo's but they are smaller.

Despite all the renovation and whitewashing, few historic buildings in Peking offer such fine harmony of form and color, so appropriate to the site, as this tomb of Yung Lo (1. Chang Ling). Only the palaces of Ch'ien Lung in the Forbidden City can stand comparison with it. You enter the precinct of temples and pavilions that make up the tomb by a great red gate that leads to a first wall-enclosed courtyard. In its middle is the *Gate of Holy Favors* (Lung En Men), one of the finest examples of classical Chinese architecture. Beyond this gate, in the middle of a second and larger courtyard, beautifully shady, there stands on a terrace of sculpted marble the finest palace of the whole precinct, the *Palace of the Holy Favors* (Lung En Tien). More than two hundred feet long, it consists of one large single hall where the emperors' writing tablets were buried. Today it is empty, supported by gigantic columns, each made from a single hardwood treetrunk. The atmosphere here is strange, with a sense of twilight and a healing freshness.

After another gate that leads to the precinct of the tomb itself, you come to a huge altar of white marble, then to the tower of the tomb or *Walled City* (Fang Cheng), which looms above the other palaces. Here the road begins that encircles the tumulus, three hundred yards in diameter, containing the vaults and catafalques where Yung Lo and the empresses Hsiao Tuan and Hsian Ching lie at rest.

You cannot visit all of the Chang Ling tomb, for the sepulchre itself is not open. You should therefore go on to the sepulchre of Ting Ling (10), which is reached down an ill-surfaced path. Its exterior buildings, though beautiful, are not especially interesting, but the vaults in the middle of the tumulus are the only remaining example of a royal tomb in a perfect state of preservation. You descend by a rather too monumental staircase, which suggests an ornate subway station; but once inside the underground palace you can see the huge gates made from a single block of marble, and beyond the hall of sacrifices, the necropolis itself, where the coffins used to lie between chests full of treasures and remarkable blue-and-white vases.

Two small museums outside the tomb house the treasures it once contained. In the more southerly one, in particular, are massive gold tiaras and fine pieces of carved jade.

The eleven other tombs are in a worse state of preservation—but each in its own way gives a charming picture of the China of bygone days. In particular you should take the road that goes around Yu Ling (4) and Yung Ling (8). You will find a superb landscape bathed in a lovely ever-changing light: fields of wheat or corn, fruit trees, *kaki* trees with their red autumn fruit, busy peasants with their donkeys and little children. Each of the thirteen tombs is worth a visit for some reason—be it a stele, a sacrificial altar, a glazed roof, or tottering vaulted arches half overgrown by trees.

The Great Wall of China

One of the wonders of the world—in the sense of being colossal and superhuman—the Great Wall can easily be reached from Peking. It is under an hour's drive away.

Begun under the Chou and finished under the T'ang, the Great Wall (Wan Li Chang Chen—the "Wall of the Ten Thousand Li") was at first a rampart of stone and earth running for over two thousand miles. Then the Ming made it a real fortification, with cement, bricks, and blocks of stone. Its purpose was to protect the Middle Kingdom from all the barbarian invaders from the north and west.

An excursion to the Great Wall will impress the most traveled of tourists. The only authorized road goes to the far limit of the Nankow Pass, where the wall, barely more than twenty feet high but seeming gigantic, stretches along either side of the summit of a deep canyon and then curves off into the far distance along the hilltops. You are allowed to walk along the top of the wall, for five hundred yards or so to the right or left. You can then climb up on to a tower and from there look at the wall curving over the mountains, its line interrupted about every two hundred yards by a stone watch-tower. Beyond it the deserted lake and the Mongolian landscape stretching into the distance are out of bounds to foreigners: the authorized road goes no farther than the tunnel piercing the wall. Similarly, in the middle of the road along the top of the wall there are signposts warning you of the limits you must not overstep.

At the foot of the wall an inn serves tea, provides shelter for a picnic in winter, and sells buns, cookies, and beer.

Before it gets to the wall, the road from Peking crosses the Chu Yung Kuan Pass. On the right is a fine marble gate, decorated all over with rare carved Buddhist friezes and inscriptions in Sanskrit, Tibetan, Tangut, Huighour, Mongol, and Chinese.

Three words of advice. First, avoid going to the Great Wall on Sundays in fine weather: part of its charm depends on its wild setting, whereas on summer Sundays it seems like any popular tourist spot anywhere in the world. Second, dress warmly in winter, for the wind from Mongolia is piercing; take not only coats and woolen clothes but also a fur cap. Finally, because the flagstones on the road on top of the wall often incline at a 45-degree angle and are frozen in winter, avoid leather soles and high heels.

The Bridge of Marco Polo

This bridge (Lu Kou Chiao) is one of the focal points of traditional Peking. Formerly a travelers' resting place, it remains a masterpiece of classical Chinese utilitarian architecture.

Ten miles southwest of Peking, its 750-foot length span the River of Mud (Hun Ho) with twelve arches in white marble. At first several wooden bridges stood here, to be replaced by a marble bridge in 1190–92, which Marco Polo saw and lyrically described. In 1698 it was carried away by a flood, but rebuilt in the same style, with two pavilions set in front of it, housing steles erected by K'ang Hsi and Ch'ien Lung. Its detail is remarkable—the parapets, and the 280 small lions, male and female, that stand in rows along the delicate line of its arches.

To get there, you leave Peking by Kuang An Men (plan, B6). Just beyond the bridge the road goes through an old walled village with narrow streets, where it is worth taking a stroll.

INDEX

INDEX

INDEX

INDEX

INDEX

INDEX

211

INDEX